Courtesan Princess

Other Books by Annette Joelson

Novels

The Dancing Girl of Gilead
Raw Clay
The Golden Stag
Desire Within
Blind Living

Biography

The Memoirs of Kohler of the
    K. W. V. (Arranged and Edited)

Historical Sketches

South African Yesterdays

Short Stories and Novellas

By Helam An Die Rivier
And Still Remember

Children's Stories

How the Ostrich Got His Name
    and Other South African Stories
Field Mouse Stories

CATHERINE GRAND
PRINCESSE DE TALLEYRAND-PÉRIGORD
by Vigée-Lebrun

Courtesan Princess

Catherine Grand, Princesse de Talleyrand

by

Annette Joelson

CHILTON BOOKS

A Division of Chilton Company
Publishers
Philadelphia and New York

This book is for my husband
Maurice Jacobs
To whom it has always belonged

Author's Note

Most of the dialogue in this book
is based on the memoirs of the
period.

Foreword

My first awareness of Catherine Grand came some thirty years ago. Panegyrized by J. J. Cotton as "Venus of the East and West" (so I discovered later), she stepped into my life not like the Botticelli Venus, from a scallop shell fringed with frilly waves, but as the result of delving into old books, old diaries, old memoirs and the yellowed pages of documents in the archives at Cape Town.

Our first meeting produced enough material for me to include her in an article about some of the interesting women who, for shorter or longer periods, had visited or stayed at the Cape of Good Hope during the eighteenth century. Much that I then disinterred, which included George François Grand's own narrative of his life in India and his Last Will and Testament with its surprising codicil, threw only a narrow beam of light on Catherine's life: on her extraordinary beauty; on the Grand v. Francis *cause célèbre;* and on the fact that, by undeservedly repudiating her, her pompous, petty, mercenary husband drove her into the arms of Philip Francis and from them onto the Dutch ship bound for England which, en route, put into Table Bay. What little I learned about Madame Grand went into that article.

But already that little was not enough. I wanted to know more, much more.

Touched by descriptions of her appealing looks, by the tragedy of so naïve a child flung pell-mell into the crushing jaws of notoriety and cynical obloquy, I found myself becoming increasingly obsessed by Catherine Grand. What was she really like as a person, this lowly born, lovely girl, "slim and tall, with very graceful carriage, a tip-tilted nose, large blue languorous eyes, a forehead of dazzling whiteness crowned with a glorious curling mass of golden hair which, loosened, reached below her knees"? What direction had her life taken after 1781 when, discarded by Grand, she stopped so briefly, a bird in flight, at Table Bay? How had she steered her course through the rough waters of the French Revolution and the era of Napoleon which brought her to anchor at last as the great Talleyrand's wife? Why had no one written a full-length book about her life? Should I attempt such a biography?

Catherine fascinated me. The period in which she lived had always been of absorbing interest to me. In short, here was something I very much wanted to do. But—there is always a but. Living as I did six thousand miles from London and Paris, would it be possible for me to harvest the material for such a book? Where should I go to seek advice?

I went to the late A. C. G. Lloyd, Chief Librarian at the South African Public Library, Cape Town. Never could I have hoped to find a better guide. He told me that day that for something like twenty years he had read everything available to him in print or manuscript about Madame Grand; that he had lived all those years with her portrait by Vigée-Lebrun in the room in which he worked.

The help Mr. Lloyd gave me was immeasurable. Limitless, too, was the aid I received from Maurice Jacobs in London whom, years later, I married. He provided me with books, pictures, notes, and photostat pages—data asked for, and very often splendid material which, but for his tireless efforts on my behalf at the British Museum and the Bibliothèque National, I might have missed. To other people who enabled me to write this book I owe thanks; in particular to Victor de Kock at the Archives in Cape Town, the late Sir Evan Cotton, and the Chief Librarian at the India Office in London who allowed books to be sent to me at the Cape.

Recently, while looking through old papers, I came upon a letter from Mr. Lloyd, written after he had read the manuscript of *Courtesan Princess*. It was moving to see his handwriting again after so many years, moving to read "You have made a serious contribution to historical biography," moving to feel that I had not utterly failed in bringing his heroine alive for him.

Annette Joelson

London, 1964

Contents

BOOK I

Prelude—*Pictures Through A Spyglass*

Pictures Through A Spyglass

I

On entering the presence of the First Consul, Monsieur de Talleyrand, Minister of Foreign Affairs, was met by a squall of words.

"No wonder we are abused and vilified by England," Bonaparte rapped out, tapping a paper which lay before him with a trembling finger. "I say it is no wonder, Monsieur de Talleyrand, when we expose ourselves to such attacks as these and even our ministers give public example of disorder and bad conduct."

Talleyrand said nothing. It was no use wasting time and breath asking questions. He was expecting a tediously long vituperative monologue and remained standing quite still, waiting, his nose in the air, his eyebrows superciliously raised.

The First Consul was extremely angry. The paper, which had been given to him earlier in the day by Fouché, contained an article grossly reviling and defaming both him and his government.

He squared his jaw pugnaciously, as his vehemence increased.

"Information has reached me that the envoys and ambassadors from foreign courts are compelled to wait upon your mistress. This must not continue, Monsieur de Talleyrand. The time for free unions is over," he thundered.

But almost as suddenly as it had begun, the storm spent itself. He continued his attack in a milder voice. Would it not be best if Monsieur de Talleyrand, formerly Bishop of Autun, once again took up the episcopal robes he had discarded with so little ceremony? Or perhaps, better still, he suggested, wouldn't his Minister of Foreign Affairs allow himself to be invested with the even more impressive purple robes of a cardinal?

Talleyrand answered courteously but firmly. Such a contingency, he regretted, was not possible. He had been thankful to escape from the priesthood. To be quite frank, nothing, nothing whatsoever, would induce him to reenter it. He did not consider himself fit for that profession.

"Very well, then, monsieur, but you must banish Madame Grand from your house." The First Consul ended the interview with a spirited ultimatum.

Talleyrand was preparing to follow Bonaparte's advice when suddenly one day he was again summoned to the presence of the First Consul. A strange change had come over Bonaparte. In issuing his second ultimatum he was much softer toward Madame Grand and much sterner with his Minister of Foreign Affairs. There was to be no quibbling with the terms of his new proposition. In twenty-four hours' time Monsieur de Talleyrand must make up his mind either to *marry* Madame Grand or to expel her from his house.

Talleyrand's eyes narrowed, but, as ever, his manner remained cold and polished as steel. Logically, volubly, dryly he argued, never for a moment laying aside his customary *sangfroid*. His objections were skillfully marshaled and enumerated. Surely, he concluded, Bonaparte must realize that marriage for a bishop, even a former one, was impossible and unthinkable.

"Monsieur de Talleyrand," answered Bonaparte unyieldingly, "the Court of the Vatican can do anything." By this he insinuated that Rome, if it wished, could even make a husband of a onetime bishop without creating much fuss and scandal. Monsieur de Talleyrand could set his mind at rest on that score, at any rate.

So there it was, almost as good as if it were written in black and white, the First Consul's final ultimatum to his Minister of Foreign Affairs. It was for Talleyrand to choose. Either he must submit to the yoke of matrimony or banish Catherine Grand from his house within twenty-four hours. For at all costs, in the year 1802, there was to be moral rectitude and orthodox conjugality in the new Court of France.

II

The spring of this year had fallen like a benediction upon Europe, bringing with it a breathing space, a respite from war. Napoleon Bonaparte, it is true, was still omnipotent on land, but Nelson was lord of the seas. For the moment the scales were evenly balanced. The Peace of Amiens was signed.

Scarcely was the ink dry on this document of temporary harmony than Paris gave herself up to pleasures and festivities. Once again she was the loveliest and liveliest of cities, seeking the admiration of the world; radiant in the luminous fireworks that played across her many bridges spanning the Seine. At night the Louvre shone like a palace on fire, the Place Vendôme twinkled with fairy lights, and the Champs Élysées blazed with prismatic colors. Through the doors of the great salons flowed the fine world of this new Paris, men and women of wit and learning, *nouveaux riches,* and people of the most opposite political principles. The theaters were crowded, particularly the Théâtre Français where Mesdemoiselles Georges and Duchesnois, "the one so good as to be beautiful, the other so beautiful as to be good," reigned supreme, enchanting the brilliant audience with their tragic genius.

At Versailles and the Tuileries that other tragedian reigned, a little pale man with an habitual stoop, fine, penetrating eyes, and a beautiful nose "such as is sometimes seen on an antique medallion"—Bonaparte, First Consul of France. It was his victories and treaties that had brought the envoys and ambassadors of Europe's greatest powers to Paris and had filled the fine salons of Josephine, of the fashionable Madame de Staël, of the fascinating Madame Récamier, and of Monsieur de Talleyrand, Minister of Foreign Affairs, with a brilliant crowd of foreigners and Frenchmen.

The most accomplished of courtiers, the most astute of diplomats, and the next important man in France after Bonaparte was this Monsieur de Talleyrand. In the Rue du Bac at the Hôtel of External Affairs, known as the Hôtel de Gallifet, and at his charming villa at Neuilly, he entertained lavishly. His *petits soupers* and *soirées*, frequented by the most illustrious personages from every court and country in Europe, were the most select in Paris.

Through the brilliant company that gathered about him, Talleyrand, dragging his crippled foot, walked with his uncertain gait, the social lion of his own salon, as he was of every salon in Paris that he visited. Now he smiled on this one, then on that; now he uttered a compliment, now some polished epigram or witty saying that in less than twenty-four hours, he knew, would be the talk of Paris.

And ever and again, but surreptitiously, his eyes—those strange eyes that sparkled anaconda-like in his cadaverous face —would wander to the end of the two long rows of armchairs running the length of the room. There at the head, tranquilly doing the honors of his house, sat Madame Grand with her lovely face and eyes, her breathtaking hair, and her little tilted nose that seemed to speak so eloquently of a thousand whims and fancies.

Like the brightest star in a galaxy Monsieur de Talleyrand's brilliance outshone that of his guests, while Madame Grand, the loveliest courtesan in Paris, in the physical perfection of her exotic grace and beauty glowed like a red-purple orchid strangely misplanted in a bed of pale pink carnations.

III

For years gossip had linked the names of Charles Maurice de Talleyrand and Catherine Noël Grand. The profligate Abbé of Périgord, former Bishop of Autun, a man with "the most scandalous career in five continents" and with "no more legs than he has heart," was the most engaging and enchanting of companions. It was unthinkable that this distinguished wit, this skillful Minister of Foreign Affairs with so excellent a taste in letters, should have succumbed so completely to the blandishments of Madame Grand, that courtesan with the beautiful face and will-o'-the-wisp whims.

Everyone was talking about Catherine Grand. Women in particular could not keep their tongues quiet. Madame de Staël said to Talleyrand one day when, in the company of friends, they were amusing themselves in a boat on the Seine: "Tell me, monsieur, whom do you like best, Madame Grand or myself?" His reply, though gracious and courtly, was equivocal and not to her satisfaction. She pressed her point further.

"Well now," she cried, "suppose we both were to fall into the water. Which would you try to save first?"

"Madame," said Talleyrand dryly, "I should be quite certain that you could swim."

Madame Grand, at this time one of the most maligned and envied women in Paris, possessed a naïve ingenuity. In her rare beauty she outshone even such rivals as Theresia Tallien and Josephine Bonaparte.

Tall and elegant, her supple figure had the soft languor habitual to women born in the East. Her hair, when loosened, fell like a golden cloak about her shoulders. Her large, languishing, intensely blue eyes resembled two fine sapphires set in her dazzling face. Gossips had much to say about her eyes. It was often asserted that they were so limpid and so strangely blue in color because of her natural gift for tears. For Catherine cried easily. Even at the slightest surprise tears sprang to her eyes and brimmed over. Yet she was never made offensive or ugly by weeping. She cried charmingly, quietly, and always convincingly.

Perhaps it was because she had reason to weep so often that Madame Grand's eyes were such a deep dark blue that summer of 1802. Bonaparte had been taken by an excess of virtue and, like leaves in a strong wind, the malicious tongues of the Faubourg Saint-Germain were fluttering with fresh rumors.

IV

The First Consul may not consciously have believed in God, but he was unquestionably convinced of the efficacy of outward respectability. With his new court in the making, he was fully determined to build it solidly upon a sound basis of regard for convention. Perfect correctness and propriety—those were to be its cornerstones.

Into the midst of this new moral order sudden grumblings and complaints in diplomatic circles fell like a bombshell. The fracas was unexpected, arising out of the fact that, about to be presented at the Hôtel of the Minister of Foreign Affairs, the wives of several ambassadors took it into their heads to turn fastidious. They balked at being received by Madame Grand. They said they were being forced to pay honor and respect to a courtesan. For some fantastic reason this thought suddenly disgusted them and they decided, even in the face of Monsieur de Talleyrand's greatness, not to demean themselves by setting foot in so disgraceful an establishment.

The mutterings, growing in volume, at last reached the ear of that serpent Fouché who, seeking as usual "to shove his dirty feet into everybody else's shoes," immediately informed the First Consul, hoping in his heart of hearts by this action to injure the power of the Minister of Foreign Affairs.

About Monsieur de Talleyrand Bonaparte had not felt quite easy in his mind of late. It was extremely awkward at a time such as this, when it was advisable to have peace between France and the Church of Rome, to have as one's Minister of Foreign Affairs an excommunicated bishop. And now, to crown all, came Fouché with grave news of discontent in diplomatic circles. That Madame Grand was Talleyrand's mistress Bonaparte knew full well, but that he should outrage convention by living publicly in open sin with so notorious a woman—that grieved him beyond measure. Something had to be done. If only he could invest Talleyrand with the cardinal's purple! How sharply and certainly would such a stratagem put an end to difficulties! But would that limp-foot Talleyrand come to heel obediently? It was doubtful, very doubtful. Still, something had to be done.

So Bonaparte had sent for Talleyrand that day of the sudden squall.

V

Meanwhile tongues in Paris had been far from still. Madame de Staël, her hair badly done in what she deemed a picturesque style, her big face redder than usual, sat down and wrote to Madame Récamier, who was spending a short time in the country. "Duroc is going to be married to Madame Hervas," she wrote, "and Madame Grand, they say, to M. de Talleyrand. Bonaparte wants everyone to be married."

What monstrous news! Monsieur de Talleyrand to marry Madame Grand!

"Ce n'est pas possible!" cried Madame de Genlis, throwing up her hands. *"Ce n'est pas possible!"* Was it not contrary to the nature of things that Talleyrand, who had said of her: "She always surrenders early to avoid scandal," should himself surrender for the same reason?

Monsieur de Talleyrand's old mother was in tears. That a Talleyrand-Périgord, the proud descendant of one of the noblest and oldest families in France, should so much as think of giving his name to a creature who had been little better than a woman of the town! So shocking a *mésalliance* was inconceivable.

"It is a whim of Talleyrand's, no doubt," they said in the Faubourg Saint-Germain. "Some ridiculous quixotic bravado."

"*Chères amies*," whispered the women confidingly, "it cannot happen. She is the sort of woman a man does not marry. Besides, she is middle-aged—forty, if she is a day."

In that last statement there was perfect and abundant truth. Catherine Grand was indeed just verging on forty. Yet she was in the prime of her great beauty. Her teeth were still magnificent. Her lips were like cherries. And though Talleyrand had been living with her for four years, and though he had not always been faithful, yet at this crucial moment she bound him to her "alike by her demands and the spell of her irresistible charms."

VI

Monsieur de Talleyrand was never liberal with his confidences. Now he walked about with his nose in the air, his neck as stiff as ever, his thin, cadaverous face a complete mask, and said nothing. Only the First Consul knew that, come what might, the odor of sanctity at his new court would not be further violated.

On September 9, 1802, very quietly, Madame Grand became Madame de Talleyrand.

In the pride and glory of her new position she looked more exquisite than ever. And well she might. She had reached the heights of her ambition. With her strange naïve ingenuity she had beguiled the mind of the greatest minister in France as, long ago in distant India, she had bewitched the hearts of George François Grand, writer in the service of John Company, and of that virulent author of the *Junius Letters,* Philip Francis, member of the Supreme Council of Bengal. For in its first ascent her star, that now shone so brightly upon the waters of the Seine, had once gleamed like an opal upon the broad bosom of the Ganges.

BOOK II

Awakening

Chapter One

I

Madame Werlée lay with her newborn baby held in the crook of her arm. The song of the sea sounded like an obbligato to her joy. How well the Tamils had named this place—Tarangambadi, "the village of the waves." Tranquebar the Danes had called it. Tranquebar. . . .

Madame Werlée, thinking of her husband Pierre, a prisoner of war and far away, tenderly caressed the infant in her arms. With sad eyes she looked down into its face. But Madame Werlée was no prophetess and so she did not read a strange destiny in that small, red, puckered face, a destiny that was to transform this little daughter of a poor seaman into Madame de Talleyrand and the future Princesse de Bénévent.

The child was born on November 21, 1762. Four days later the names of Catherine Noël were given to her in the tiny Roman Catholic parish church of Tranquebar. Her baptismal certificate was written out in Portuguese.

Tranquebar, on the Coromandel Coast not very far from Pondicherry, was a Danish settlement and the first and earliest stronghold of Protestant missionaries in India. But Catherine was neither a Protestant nor Danish. Neither was she Portuguese, though her initiation into the Christian community had been recorded in that language. Both her parents were Catholic and French. Her father, Pierre Werlée, a seafaring Breton who had come out to India in his youth, had been until just before her birth Lieutenant du Port at Pondicherry and a servant of the king of France; her mother, Laurence Alleigne, was the daughter of a master armorer in the employment of the French Company.

Pierre Werlée was a widower when he married Laurence. He had married his first wife, fourteen-year-old Marguerite da Silva, when he was just twenty-three. At the time of his first marriage he was already a master pilot of the Ganges stationed at Chandernagore, chief center of the French in Bengal, situated twenty miles from Calcutta on the right bank of the Hooghly river.

Those were stirring days in India. Dupleix, the hero of the French, and that young Englishman Robert Clive, were each trying to sow the seeds of a great empire for their respective countries. But at this time the brilliant Frenchman had been called home in disgrace, leaving Clive to go from strength to strength, to crush Surajah Dowlah at Plassey and capture Chandernagore.

In the hands of the English Chandernagore was no place for a servant of His Majesty of France, and Pierre Werlée was forced to separate himself from his family for several years. He was still absent when Marguerite died at Chandernagore, barely a decade after their marriage. She had been a good wife to him and bore him four children.

When peace was signed between the English and the French, Pierre arrived at Pondicherry and received the office of Lieutenant du Port. Here, in 1758, he married the master armorer's daughter.

Soon after his marriage hostilities with England broke out again. Laurence and her four stepchildren went to live at Tranquebar and Pierre's name appeared in a list of French prisoners of war sent for exchange to the Isle of France.

Catherine, the first child of his second marriage, was born during these perilous times, and in his absence.

That night at Tranquebar, Catherine Noël Werlée, who was to witness the rise and fall of empires and the beginning and end of many a great man's career, opened her eyes on a world which already seemed to be waiting for the laying of that cornerstone of modern democracy, the French Revolution. It was a world gasping for essential changes in morals and governments, but which, for all that, still allowed hideous corruption to sit on the doorstep of glittering splendor. And the character and fortune of these times into which she was born were, in a great measure, to shape and decide the strange course of her life.

II

The fortunes of war kept Pierre Werlée far from his home, and it was not till peace restored Chandernagore to the French establishment in India that he was again united with his family. Then, for the first time, he set eyes on his daughter Catherine.

Pierre Werlée was now appointed Capitaine du Port at Chandernagore, at a salary of two thousand two hundred rupees a year. In addition, the Company allowed him to indulge in a little private business. At last he was in fairly comfortable circumstances. He established his family in a roomy and pleasant house where, when Catherine was four years old, her brother Jean Xavier was born.

Catherine was one of a family of six. She had two half-brothers, two half-sisters, and a brother. Of these Marie, her eldest half-sister, and Jean Xavier, her brother, lived to be people of some position in India. Jean Xavier became a Chevalier de la Légion d'Honneur and the wealthy owner of a thriving indigo concern at Harrah. Marie, who was for some years at least to remain closer to Catherine than perhaps any other member of her family, married Michel Nicolas de Calnois, a man of good position, Chief Notary Public at Chandernagore and son of the Senior Councillor in the French service.

Chapter Two

I

For the first years of her life Catherine passed her days in a blissful world. In the mornings she played with her dolls, long-legged wooden creatures with painted cheeks which, for all their gaucherie, she adored. In the afternoons, gowned in a billowing dress, a beribboned bonnet on her curly head, she was taken for a walk. At such times, in her quaint attire, she was an exact and perfect miniature of her mother. She fancied herself most in her best gown of blue silk, trimmed with pink ribbons. Attired in this dress, she would stand for long minutes preening herself with grave infant vanity before a mirror. For Catherine, like all children of her time, was precocious. She was a lovely, lighthearted little creature, born for sunshine and happiness, dainty as a bit of thistledown.

When she grew a little older her education began. Her mother taught her to read and to write, to know her catechism and to sing a few airs, promising, too, that some day she might learn to play upon the harp. This, as far as it went, was not a very inspiring education, but then she was, after all, only the daughter of a government official and not the male heir of a great family destined to carry through the world the proud banner of fortune and fame. Her destiny, like that of all girls of her period, was matrimony, to which she would have to give herself dutifully when the time came. The time came early in those days. Girls were married in extreme youth, almost in child-hood. To be eighteen and unmarried was to be an old maid.

But if her education was unexacting and trivial in respect to learning, it was, when she grew a little older, profound and extremely thorough with regard to the social graces. By the time she was thirteen Catherine had made herself mistress of all the "airs and elegances of established fashion." She had studied the correct affectations of gesture and carriage, and was proficient in the art of smiles and nods, dimplings and poutings. She knew how to take the floor and dance a graceful measure.

She had made herself mistress of the fine art of the fan, too, so that "one instant it whispered invitingly as it played over her mischievous lips and laughing eyes," and the next, "in a sudden flash of temper," she could make it snap out "a reprimanding 'Prithee, no more.'" In a hundred other tricks she was expert. She held her head superbly high, ate like a pecking bird, drank with fluttering lashes, blew her small impertinent nose most daintily, and warbled delicate little airs in a charming flutelike treble.

She was lithe and lovely at this age—a Dresden china figure with delicate, fine-boned features and the body of a nymph. Her neck was long and tapering, her hair massed in lively wanton curls. Her unusual eyes gave her face a variety of expressions. Her nose, slightly tilted, was as pretty as could be. She was the quintessence of delicate childish elegance and mature sophisticated allurement.

For so enchanting a little creature an entrée into that polite society which whirled through the grand portals of Ghyretti House, the home of the French governor Monsieur Chevalier, was assured. Catherine Werlée became the belle of Chandernagore.

II

There were no hill stations to which Europeans could escape during the summer heat in the days when Warren Hastings was Governor-General of Bengal and Philip Francis the next most important member on the Supreme Council of India. Instead of the hills, the residents of Calcutta sought cool air and fresh breezes by going up the Hooghly river to one or other of the settlements that had sprung up on its banks. Serampore, an old

Danish outpost, was one of the most popular of these holiday resorts, not alone because of the excellence of its famous Denmark Tavern but also because of its proximity to Chandernagore.

With peace between England and France, those were the golden days of Chandernagore, and Jean Baptiste Chevalier, visionary and most adventurous and cultured of gentlemen, Knight of the Royal and Military Order of St. Louis, was its illustrious governor. He made Chandernagore a prosperous outpost of France, turning it socially into a veritable Paris in India. And when, a year after making the charming Marie Anne de la Tremblaye his wife, he built his famous country residence, Ghyretti House, it was said to rival in splendor and magnificence the very glories of Versailles.

Even if this was an exaggeration, one thing was certain: the garden house of Ghyretti, situated a few miles to the south of Chandernagore, was indeed one of the finest buildings in India. High walls surrounded the magnificent house, its splendid gardens, its huge circular courtyard, and its spacious stables which could amply accommodate a hundred horses. The road swept through the great gateway, to pass down a grand avenue of tall trees, ending at the massive front portico ornamented with an Ionic peristyle in the Greek manner.

No less beautiful than its exterior was the interior of Ghyretti House. Here were ceilings painted by a master hand, wonderful cornices, and statuary of rare beauty. The salon was of magnificent proportions, the hall thirty-six feet high. But perhaps the greatest splendor of all was the wide sweeping staircase, grand in conception, noble in its proportions.

Dignified and majestic was this palace of Ghyretti. The Bengalese even made a proverb about it, saying that in its great courtyard rose both the sun and the moon. Governor Chevalier called it his *Jardin de l'amitié,* and in it, with pomp and circumstance, he entertained great assemblies at suppers, balls, and routs. On such occasions hundreds of gay equipages, carriages, phaetons, and palanquins blocked the long, wide avenue. In the great hall fine gentlemen and ladies supped and danced with gaiety and gallantry. Laughter echoed from room to room. On white moon-lit nights lovers flitted like happy ghosts among the tall trees in the garden, and often from the summerhouse sheltered in dark, protecting shadows, came the throbbing plaints of passion-ate serenades.

All the beauty and fashion of Chandernagore, Serampore, and other neighboring settlements were invited to this Indian Versailles. Here, too, from Calcutta came the cream of society, glittering with splendor, to partake of the lavish Gallic hospitality of Monsieur Chevalier. Indeed, even such august representatives of English sovereignty in India as Warren Hastings, Philip Francis, and Richard Barwell set aside their private and political quarrels to honor with their presence some ball or rout or banquet at Ghyretti House.

In their green-painted budgerows they came down the river from Calcutta with all speed. Frequently on such occasions they were accompanied by great ladies. Hastings brought Marian, she of the auburn hair and countenance of gentle childlike simplicity, and young Mrs. Motte, her inseparable friend, who was Mary Touchet before her marriage. Lady Chambers, whom Dr. Samuel Johnson had deemed "exquisitely beautiful" when, as a very young girl, he knew her in England, came with her husband Sir Robert, Judge of the Supreme Court of Bengal. Richard Barwell brought delightful Mrs. Barwell, who had once sat for Sir Joshua Reynolds as model for his Hebe, and whom many a gentleman had worshiped when, as the celebrated Miss Sanderson, she was the toast of Calcutta.

It was, indeed, a gay and gallant company that flitted in and out of the hospitable portals of Ghyretti House, to which, on occasion, Monsieur Chevalier invited that enchantingly lovely child Catherine Noël Werlée. Rather overfine company for the daughter of a one-time Breton seafaring man. However, Pierre Werlée was at this time the much-respected Capitaine du Port, and one of his daughters, Marie, had contracted a good marriage with Michel Nicolas de Calnois, Chief Notary Public. Above all, Catherine herself was beautiful as Venus. This child, less than fifteen years of age, outrivaled in exquisiteness of face and figure and grace of carriage the finest ladies of the grand society to which, upon occasion, Monsieur Chevalier invited her.

III

At Ghyretti House Catherine first set eyes on the tall handsome figure and fine classical features of Philip Francis, member of the Supreme Council of Bengal. It was here, too, one night, that she made the acquaintance of a certain gentleman in the employment of the British East India Company, George François Grand.

Grand had but recently arrived in Calcutta from Madras, the bearer of dispatches for the Governor-General from Colonel Macleane. Hastings, whom he had met some years before, had received him with great courtesy and kindness and had expressed the wish that the young man should consider himself an intimate associate of the Governor's household. Extremely happy in his new surroundings, Grand struck up a pleasant friendship with the military and private secretaries, Major William Palmer and Major Gall, and, indeed, performed a considerable amount of clerical work for Hastings, spending many hours in the writing room of the Presidency, busily occupied in copying out official dispatches and secret papers.

As a result of his association with the Governor-General's family, Grand met all the people of fashionable Calcutta society, even haughty Francis with his superior airs and face of bronze. The beautiful houses on Garden Reach opened their doors to him. He often dined with the Barwells and during dinner pelted many a pink cheek with little bread pills, *à la mode de Bengale,* for this was a game much in vogue with people of *ton* in Calcutta.

He went, too, to balls, and to the races, and to that scene of riotous and noisy festivity and convivial carousals, the Harmonic

Tavern. For a gold mohur he watched from a seat in a box the latest production at the theater, and on many a moonlight night joined a walking party to stroll beside the dark silent river, along that portion of the paddy-covered "maidan" known as the Esplanade. Sometimes, too, in a budgerow, he went up the river at night with a company of friends in search of cooling breezes. Under the starry Indian sky the gaily painted barge crept up the stream, its lights reflected in the dark ripples of the water. On board there was gaiety, voices raised in song, and the harmony of musical instruments—viols and the thin sweet sighs of oboes and the pleasant rich tones of clarinets.

Often, too, at the end of a long week of work, Grand and his two good friends, Major Palmer and Major Gall, made longer excursions up the Hooghly. Their favorite weekend refuge was the home of Mr. Croft, owner of a large sugarcane plantation at Sooksagur. One day they went still further on to Chandernagore. Upon hearing of their arrival, and because of his friendship for Hastings, Monsieur Chevalier extended the hospitality of his famous mansion to the two gentlemen of the English governor's household and to their companion, the writer in the service of John Company.

Again and again, after this, the gaiety and delight of Ghyretti House drew the three friends up the river from Calcutta at the end of a hard week's work. So it happened, at last, that George François Grand met Catherine Noël Werlée, of whose beauty, already celebrated beyond the bounds of Chandernagore, he had heard such glowing accounts.

Chapter Three

I

The great hall of Ghyretti House was crowded that night with a brilliant gathering. Wide doors stood open to the cool night breezes; hundreds of candles blazing in massive chandeliers and gilded sconces set shadows dancing on the smooth high walls.

Near the foot of the great staircase, her gown of diaphanous blue accentuating the creamy whiteness of her skin and the vivid crimson of her lips, her eyes dancing and her laughter rippling, stood Catherine Werlée. A posy of blood-red roses nestled in the lace upon her breast. She wore no jewelry. In her slender hands she held a tiny ivory fan which she used charmingly.

Her head held high, the golden hair framing the perfect oval of her face, she made a picture to dazzle the eyes of the most jaded of men. At sight of her George François Grand, writer in the employment of the British Company, capitulated completely. In that first instant of glimpsing her, he asked to be presented. He kissed her fingertips and, drawing her hand through his arm, led her up the staircase at his side.

They danced; they talked. The night wore on to dawn. At last the time came for George to go. When he took his leave she raised her eyes to his. Entranced, he stood gazing into their blue depths. A sharp little tap of her fan on his wrist brought him to his senses.

"Forgive me, mademoiselle," he murmured gravely.

His pompous weightiness filled her with a strange mixture of awe and gentle amusement. "For what do you apologize, monsieur?" she asked softly, tantalizingly, provocatively.

24

"For keeping you standing here so long that I may look my fill into the loveliest eyes in India," he answered with clumsy gallantry. He stooped and kissed her hand and the next moment was gone.

Deep in thought, Catherine stood tapping her small foot. A strange, plain, unprepossessing and rather dull man, this Mr. Grand, with his stiff, staid, heavy manner. Yet there was something kind and solid and dependable about him. She rather liked him. She really rather liked him. . . .

Again and again Grand came to Ghyretti House, and then one day he called to pay his respects to Monsieur Pierre Werlée, the Capitaine du Port, and his good wife. . . . They said in Chandernagore that George Grand laid siege to Catherine Werlée's heart like an elephant wooing a rose.

In the end he had his way. When he heard from her at last of the tender feelings that she had for him, he fell on his knees and kissed the hem of her gown. For a moment the stiff and pompous Grand was quite overwrought. Then he was on his feet again. He pressed her head against his shoulder. He felt as though he had conquered the world, and, indeed, never before in all his life had he experienced such happiness.

Though there was great disparity in the ages of Catherine and her suitor—Grand being very nearly twice as old as she—the old Capitaine du Port gave them his blessing gladly. He approved of Grand's family, particularly of his maternal grandfather who had been a seigneur of France in the days of Louis XIV. With due ceremony the betrothal was announced, Monsieur Werlée promising that the wedding might take place just as soon as Grand had obtained a situation that would better enable him to set up a pleasant and suitable home for Catherine. The young man was by no means a penniless lover, for he did have a writership in the British company. Nevertheless his future father-in-law, ever a shrewd man, deemed his material position far from satisfactory.

George, anxious to possess forever the prize he had won, set to work with all haste to improve his station in life.

Hyde. The "Lady Governess," with her infantile airs, continually smiled into the double-chinned face of the Chief Justice, Sir Elijah Impey. For all her ostentation in dress—for she was gowned rather in the manner of a European lady masquerading as an Eastern princess—Mrs. Hastings was an engaging little lady. Many remembered her from the days when she was only the wife of the German painter Imhoff.

Mrs. Wheler created a furor as she danced in a wide hooped skirt with Mr. Grand. Mrs. Hyde, a gifted musician and prime favorite in society who was sitting in a corner with George Shee, Major Palmer, Major Gall, and the dwarfish Gerard Ducarel, broke off in the middle of an animated discourse on the instrumental creations of Bach to praise the elegance of Mrs. Wheler's magnificent hoop. At that moment Francis bent slightly toward Catherine. "I have never seen the like in all my life," he whispered, and, though his words referred to Mrs. Wheler's hoop, his eyes spoke of things his lips dared not utter.

III

Among those ladies and gentlemen of Bengal society, a society in which—perhaps because of the dreadful climate or because, like Francis, many people suffered from "the bile"—there seethed enough malice and gossip to fill a whole continent. Calcutta was a hotbed of social and political intrigue. Not a day passed without some great or lesser scandal. Always Lady Impey was, metaphorically, at the throat of Mrs. Hyde, and Francis, quite literally, at the throat of Hastings. The thoughts of ladies were of lovers and husbands, and most gentlemen believed, among a great many other things, that "I trust you with my wife, you trust me with yours" was a premier axiom of gallantry.

Into this atmosphere of social brilliance and mixed passions, of political enmity and personal intrigues, George François Grand had brought his beautiful child wife.

III

His mind fixed on the power and glory of wealth, George Grand went about his daily duties quite oblivious of the drama that was being enacted almost under his nose. His sight was, no doubt, a little impaired these days by the fog of his debts of honor. Ever an indefatigable gambler, he had recently plunged into high play at the card tables, with very indifferent success. Money was in his blood. In the hope of retrieving his losses, he spent many evenings of the week gaming at some tavern in town or at Barwell's house in Alipore. On such occasions he left Catherine alone, to amuse herself as best she could by reading or chattering with her ayah.

So the months slipped by, and again the deadly season of heat and disease came to Calcutta. Influenza raged; mosquitoes brought their burden of malaria; mysterious fevers took their hideous toll. The undertakers were busy and doctors, fighting death with physic, blistering, and bloodletting, went hurrying in their palanquins from house to house, at a charge of one gold mohur for every visit. It was this season of misery and universal sorrow that carried poor Mrs. Wheler to her grave after but seven months' residence in Calcutta, and brought the untimely death of that accomplished and lively lady, Mrs. Richard Barwell. Deeply and sincerely mourned, she was laid to rest in the South Park Street Burying Ground, Calcutta's Père Lachaise. With her passing Catherine lost a kind and generous friend.

A gloom hung over the settlement. Francis wrote to Sir John Day in Madras: "I hate the thought, for my part, of dying of the spleen like a rat in a hole. If I had given way to it heretofore I should now have been stretched alongside of Clavering and Monson with a damned *hic jacet* upon my heart. I have many reasons for not wishing to die in Bengal."

The First Councillor was in a mood of deepest depression. The

II

Grand was a servant of the British India Company, though he was not an Englishman. His maternal grandfather, the Seigneur de Virly, had fled from France at the revocation of the Edict of Nantes to take refuge in England. There his daughter married a gentleman from Switzerland named Grand. Their son George François was born on the shores of Lake Geneva and was educated at the University of Lausanne. Unfortunately Grand senior was not a wealthy man. As times grew worse and his family larger, he found it necessary to send George François to England as an apprentice to Robert Jones of Clement's Lane, London, in order that the youth might learn to become a British merchant.

Finely dressed in laced and embroidered clothes, a sword by his side and a *chapeau bras* on his curled and pigtailed head, young Grand arrived in London. Such refinement did not please Jones, who immediately had the lad's pigtail cropped and his hair cut close. Instead of his charming clothes, the young Swiss was made to wear a plain English suit and a stupid round hat upon his head. "I do it for your own good," declared the gruff Jones, "so that people might not take you for a French monkey imported onto English ground."

This new life in the counting-house was a great change from the fine assemblies in Lausanne to which once he had accompanied his reverend tutor. Here he had to clean the room and dust the desks and chairs, tend the fire and run errands about the city streets. Small wonder that his days were spent in unhappiness and disgust and that, at the very first opportunity, he left the premises of Robert Jones and the uncongenial environs of Clement's Lane. Fortunately for him, an aunt in England took a kindly interest in his welfare. With her assistance he secured a cadetship in Bengal and in the company of eleven writers—among them a William Thackeray who was to become the grandfather of a famous novelist—he sailed for India.

Grand landed at Madras and from there proceeded to Calcutta, where he was received by Clive. Considering the cadet too
youthful to be entrusted with a commission, Clive sent him to
join the second brigade. Grand, however, was a young man of
ambition and determination and very soon received a commission
as ensign, signed by the great Clive himself. Seven years later, he
gained the rank of captain.

The Indian climate, however, had played havoc with the
young captain's health and now, anxious to regain the "sound-
ness of his body," he decided to take a holiday trip to England.
Sailings unfortunately were few and far between, and he was
forced to wait three months in Calcutta for a passage on the
Marquis of Rookingham. The time passed quickly enough for
the young officer, since, as guest of his good friend General
Anthony Pollier, he joined in all the gaieties of the capital of
English Bengal. The new governor, Warren Hastings, showed
him great friendliness.

On many occasions, too, he met that much discussed couple,
the painter Imhoff and his wife. Tongues in Calcutta were wagging about this engaging woman. It was said that the Governor-
General was filled with a deep, strong and unconquerable passion
for her; and for once the chattering tongues were right. When
at last the *Marquis of Rookingham* set sail from India, Imhoff
was one of Grand's fellow travelers. His lady remained behind.
The Imhoffs and the Governor had reached an amicable agree-
ment and Imhoff was on his way to Europe to arrange a divorce
so that Mrs. Imhoff, when matters had been satisfactorily settled,
might marry Warren Hastings.

Grand reached England safely, to enjoy a well-earned holiday.
Then, completely restored to health, he applied for and obtained
a writership in the British India Company and once again arrived
in Madras. It was at this time, after having been sent by Colonel
Macleane to Calcutta with official dispatches for the Governor-
General, that he met Catherine Noël Werlée.

III

George Grand had many influential friends in Calcutta. With all haste he began to set in motion the machinery that would enable him to overcome the only stumbling block to his marriage with the bewitching daughter of the Capitaine du Port at Chandernagore.

First he approached his kind friend Richard Barwell, who, allied politically with Hastings, formed the opposition in the Supreme Council of Bengal against that dark-tempered reformer Philip Francis. When informed in detail by Grand of his anxieties and tribulations, Barwell showed himself both understanding and sympathetic. He would be delighted to help smooth the lover's rough path. "Indeed, my dear Grand, I am most desirous to alleviate the sufferings of a young couple so ardent to be united," he declared wholeheartedly.

He gave advice—sane, practical advice. It would be politic, he assured Grand, to go directly to the Governor-General and inform him of the troublesome position. "Furthermore," declared Barwell, "I assure you, my dear Grand, that whatever Hastings can devise for your welfare will meet with my hearty concurrence."

Hastings, the kindest and most generous of men, listened with lively compassion to Grand. A position which would have suited Grand admirably, that of paymaster to the garrisons, had just become vacant, but unfortunately it was already promised to another gentleman.

By a process of reshuffling offices Hastings and Barwell managed to obtain for Grand not only the secretaryship of the Salt Committee, but also the position of Head Assistant and Examiner to the Board of Trade's Secretary, Charles Grant. Between them these two situations insured a monthly income of thirteen hundred rupees, and Grand felt that at last he had the right to claim

Catherine. Monsieur Werlée, her father, willingly agreed to fix a date for the marriage.

Since Catherine was a Catholic and George a Protestant, it was necessary for their union to be solemnized with two ceremonies. The first, legalized by a priest, was performed in the Roman Catholic parish church of Chandernagore on July 10, 1777, at the extraordinarily irregular hour of one o'clock in the morning. The second, performed by the English chaplain, the Reverend William Johnson, by special license from the Governor-General, took place seven hours later in a private house at Hooghly. It was the home of an old Benares friend of the bridegroom, Thomas Motte, husband of Mary Touchet, the intimate of the former Mrs. Imhoff, who had recently become the "Lady Governess."

Grand's marriage with Mademoiselle Werlée began with the happiest augury, for contrary to the general rule in the society of Bengal where the prize in most cases went to the highest bidder, Cupid did indeed wait upon Hymen. Catherine, just three months short of fifteen years of age, loved her humorless and often querulous husband and returned his mature and passionate affection with the simple tenderness of a child. It was in truth, as Grand declared, a union "blessed with the sincerest reciprocal attachment."

A new life now began for the daughter of Monsieur Pierre Werlée. Mrs. Grand she was now called—Mrs. and not Madame, since Grand was an Englishman by adoption. Radiantly happy, a loving child wife clinging trustingly to the arm of her fussy, pompous husband, she entered the gay and brilliant society of Calcutta in which Warren Hastings, the courteous and refined first gentleman of British India, played the leading role and Philip Francis that of the ill-tempered angel of discord in the paradise of Bengal.

BOOK III

La Belle Indienne

Chapter One

I

Calcutta, official capital of British India, seat of the govern-
ing Council and the Supreme Court, spread itself along the
eastern bank of the Hooghly river, tributary of the Ganges.
Though the Mahratta Ditch, zigzagging across malarial swamps,
marked the limits of the Supreme Council's jurisdiction, the
Chilpore Road, running north to south and cutting off the Lall
Bazar from Bow Bazar and Esplanade Row from Durrumbullah
Street, formed the actual boundary of the European section of
the town, of which Tank Square was the hub.

It was a town of Eastern elegance and appallingly unsanitary
conditions. The streets were in wretched condition. Packs of
mangy prowling pariah dogs were to be seen everywhere. Myr-
iads of flies bred in open cesspools. Diseased fakirs paraded the
town. Hindus carried their naked dead, loosely tied to long bamboo poles, through the streets, and flung the corpses into the
purifying waters of the Hooghly, where they were left either to
rot and infect the stream or be eaten by scavenging birds and
crocodiles.

Strewn with dead bodies of men and beasts the river presented
a gruesome spectacle and formed a malignant nursery for all
manner of diseases. Even Calcutta's fresh water supply was not
free from pollution, but very wisely, in an effort to prevent going down with "a putrid fever or a flux," most Europeans
slaked their unquenchable summer thirst with mulled claret,
Madeira wines, and arrack punch.

Despite the town's unhygienic condition and a life bur-
dened with more than its share of human suffering and misery,
of sickness, bloodletting, and blistering, the society into which

George François Grand introduced his young wife lived in great style and state. Homes were large, rooms spacious and airy, furniture elegant to a degree.

The Governor-General had his official residence on Esplanade Row, next to the Council House; Philip Francis owned a house just behind the Playhouse, and lived there when he was in town; Sir Elijah Impey, the Chief Justice, possessed a fine mansion and a deer park not very far from the Burying Ground. Besides, there were beautiful residences surrounded by large compounds on Garden Reach and a whole quarter of fashionable homes in Post Office Street.

Calcutta was an opulent town. There was much money to be made and, while little time was occupied by work, a great deal of it was spent on social activities. In the hope of forgetting the cruelties of the Indian climate with its accompanying ills, people of fashion gave themselves up to gaiety and a ridiculously unsuitable style of living.

Any and every occasion was considered an excuse for convivial routs and festivities. Banquets were held in October to celebrate the conclusion of the season of death and disease. With much merriment, on these occasions members of society rejoiced at the fact that they were still aboveground and not, like so many of their good friends, four feet below the Indian earth in the Burying Ground near Mission Row.

For people of *ton* in Calcutta, the day began in the early morning with a ride or a walk. At nine o'clock came breakfast, a *dégagé* meal, for which informal dress was worn. Since this was the time for gentlemen to call quite unconventionally, ladies took care to look particularly charming in negligees. The hours from breakfast to noon were given over to business and the hairdresser. Robed in white jackets, gentlemen sat leisurely smoking their long-tubed hookahs while they listened in comfort to the latest gossip retailed by their friseurs. At home, while their heads were being dressed with powder, gauze, and flowers, ladies chattered amiably or read the latest chit brought by a bearer from a friend.

At two o'clock came dinner. Even in the most trying weather this was an enormous meal of endless courses—soup, roast fowl, curries, mutton pies, forequarters of lamb, puddings, tarts, freshly churned butter, cheese, bread, and delectable wines. Two glasses were set at every place, one for Madeira, the other for claret and white wines. At the end of the meal, when already a few loyal healths had been drunk, the ladies withdrew. But dinner was by no means over. No gentleman dreamed of getting up from the table before he had emptied at least three bottles of red or white wine.

To mitigate the effects of dinner, the afternoon was given up to a long siesta. Both sexes undressed completely and went to bed as if the time were midnight. Then, for hours, Calcutta lay in heat and silence. People awakened only when the hairdresser came to pay his second call. With deft fingers he retouched sleep-crushed coiffures in readiness for sundown. Now the streets broke into life again and society, looking cool and elegant, set out on gentle promenades along the Esplanade or for drives across the Race Course. Upon returning from these outings, it was customary for ladies to pay short formal and friendly visits to each other, and, after a hasty cup of tea or coffee, to hurry home in order to receive their own callers.

Gentlemen paid visits only after the tea hour was over. If asked by a hostess to lay aside their hats during the call, an invitation to stay for supper was implied. This meal was never served before ten o'clock, but the hours of waiting passed quickly, for there was always music and card playing to fill the time.

For an evening to end before midnight was considered the height of plebeianism. Night was meant for revelry, and if there was no dancing or music, there was either card playing or pleasant conversation and hookah smoking. A gentleman always took his *houccabardar* with him wherever he went. It was the duty of this servant to feed the hookah and keep it burning with his breath.

European ladies of fashion occasionally enjoyed a smoke. Indeed, for a lady to desire a puff from a gentleman's hookah was an expression of delicate flattery. Immediately then, according to the rules of politeness and etiquette, the gentleman would place a new mouthpiece into the long tube, or snake, and gallantly present it to her. He would watch her as she drew the smoke into her mouth, preening himself all the while, for, having paid him such a compliment, there was no knowing with what further favors she might yet honor him. . . .

Catherine Grand played a lively part in the entertainments held in private houses. She attended, too, the balls and formal dinners given by the Burra Sahibs of Calcutta, Warren Hastings and his colleagues on the Council and the august judges of the Supreme Court. In addition she frequently enjoyed the delights of public masquerades, sat watching while the gentlemen amused themselves at the card tables, and herself played an occasional game of whist.

Play at cards ran high in Calcutta and many a fortune was made and lost at five-card loo and whist. On nights of high play, however, ladies were seldom present. These were essentially occasions for stag parties. The most favored place for gaming was some fashionable tavern in the town, but, at least once a week, Barwell entertained his men friends at dinner and cards at his lodge near Alipore. It was there that George Grand lost large portions of his salary while Francis, playing with skill and phenomenal luck, often won several hundred pounds a night.

As gay and lavish as its pleasures was the fashionable dress of Calcutta society: lace, spangles, and foil-decorated velvet suits and gowns of silk and brocade. Even the conveyances spoke of Eastern elegance and opulent riches. The Hooghly budgerows looked every whit as grand as state barges on the Thames; phaetons and carriages, drawn by finely caparisoned horses, glistened with ornamentation; palanquins, fantastically curtained and cushioned sedan chairs, were carried high on the shoulders of black servants. As they picked their way down the streets, the bearers uttered the strangest of noises. These sounds did not indicate fatigue but were commentaries on the state of the roads. In a singsong they would cry out: "Here's a puddle of water"; "Here's a heap of stones"; "There's a hole," till the air was full of their warnings.

II

There were many individual ladies and gentlemen of the brilliant society of Calcutta who, in one way or another, were to play a part in the life of Catherine Grand. At a ball given in honor of Mr. and Mrs. Wheler, newly arrived from England, Catherine mingled with most of those who were her world now. Mr. Wheler had come to fill that position on the Supreme Council left vacant by the recent death of the pugnacious General Clavering.

Warren Hastings, amiable and unaffected, was as simple in his manner as his dress. When he smiled it was difficult to realize how bitterly he was waging war against the vexations of his arduous political life and the machinations of Philip Francis, his avowed antagonist in the councils of government.

When, at this ball, the *cotillon* ended, Francis claimed a dance from Catherine. Ten years earlier he was called *le bel Anglais* in Paris. In Calcutta his haughty airs earned him the name of "King Francis the First." He was extraordinarily handsome and well endowed with all the charms most appealing to women. Ladies, even the wives of his political enemies, admired him greatly. . . .

Richard Barwell danced with Mrs. Motte. Barwell, onetime friend of Dr. Samuel Johnson and Boswell, and the Governor-General's staunchest ally in the Council, was close to both George and Catherine. In all their married life the Grands had no better friend than Richard Barwell. His wife, to whose fascination when she was the celebrated Miss Sanderson, Grand had fallen in vain, danced that night with friendly natured Sir Robert Chambers, while Lady Chambers accompanied Justice

IV

For the first ten months of their married life the Grands lived with old Robert Sanderson, father-in-law of their good friend Richard Barwell. They were, to outward appearance, an incongruous couple. George, with a heart full of passion and a tongue devoid of wit, was a heavy mannered gentleman, while Catherine was all daintiness and lightness. Yet, in spite of the contrast of their personalities, they were absurdly happy together.

Catherine entered wholeheartedly into the fascinating game of being Mrs. Grand of Calcutta for, despite her society graces and accomplishments, she was little more than a naïve and playful child. Viewing the world through rose-colored glasses, it seemed to her that never before had there lived a person so happy as she now was. Everything in her new life delighted her, particularly George, who was completely under the spell of her beauty.

George found it difficult to deny her anything. She looked so enchanting when she coaxed and pleaded, so appealing when, under her dark brows, her blue eyes filled with tears. Not even her ridiculous whim, to visit the teeming native bazaars in the early morning, could he refuse to gratify. He did argue strongly against it for a while, scolding her a little and explaining grandiloquently that there were enough European shops to satisfy anyone's craving, and people of *ton* did not visit such places in Calcutta. For answer she merely looked at him beseechingly, climbed on his knee, pressed her cheek against his face, and whispered into his ear. In the end he not only took her to the native bazaars one early morning, but once there, bought her innumerable gifts—Arab dainties, Turkish sweetmeats, and a cashmere shawl that a Bengalese salesman praised in words of poetry.

George Grand found himself enjoying every moment of this escapade with Catherine walking at his side. It gave him a sensual satisfaction to watch her fingers caressing the texture of English broadcloths, Persian brocades, and fine silks from Benares and Moorshedabad. He smiled amusedly when she went into ecstasies over some trifling beads from the Coromandel Coast or a jewel from Bundelcund. Nothing escaped her eyes. She reacted physically to everything. Even her nose seemed to quiver with excitement as she sniffed the odor of spices from the Straits and stooped to smell the fragrance of myrrh and frankincense from Ceylon.

They enjoyed these and other pleasures together those first months of their marriage. Many a night they dined at one or other of the fine houses on Garden Reach or Alipore. They went to the Playhouse even though she knew only a few words of English and understood but little of the play itself. Everything delighted her—the dress and movements of the company of male actors as much as the winking candles in their sconces, the new fashion in which Mrs. Hastings had dressed her hair for the occasion, and the splendid jewels displayed by the highborn Indian ladies in their boxes. . . .

In the evening after the day's heat, the setting sun was the signal for society to take the air. Frequently Catherine and George joined a budgerow party on the Hooghly. More often still, they set off in a carriage for a drive along the Course, the three-mile race ground on the tree studded maidan. Though a dusty evening's airing in dry weather, it was nevertheless a pleasurable one. So many things happened there. It was there that one heard—or watched the beginnings—of the most exciting scandals. The Course was a veritable field of love. Words whispered to a lady by an indiscreet beau as he stood on the footsteps of her chariot often reached other ears besides her own!

When the Grands did not go up the river or driving on the Course, they walked along the Esplanade or around the formal fish lake and sweet-water cisterns in Tank Square—that popular resort for social assembly, facing the Old Fort with its tragic memories of the Black Hole. But the Esplanade itself was Catherine's favorite walk. Especially did it enchant her when darkness fell and the link boys, calling their quaint cry of "tok-tok," came running along to meet their masters. In the black Indian night, the moving lights of their flambeaux produced a fairy-like effect that was eerie and yet pleasantly romantic.

But greatest of all her delights was dancing. Such exciting nights those were when George took her to a ball. She stepped daintily through *cotillons*, minuets, and country dances. No sooner did the music stop than, like bees around a honey jar, partners flocked around her, eager for the honor of dancing with her. She was careful and observed the rules of etiquette, and gave not more than two dances to any gentleman but her husband. She looked enchanting on these nights of revelry, with flowers entwined in her hair and her eyes shining as brightly as the lights that set fine jewels twinkling.

The music and the dancing ceased only at an hour near dawn. Then, in a palanquin hoisted on the shoulders of hurrying bearers, Catherine rode back to her home. Sometimes, wide-awake with excitement, she would gaze into the quiet night, and sometimes, at the sight of a poor widow being carried off to suttee down the street, she would weep bitterly. But more often than not, when home was reached she was sound asleep and George had to carry her up the stairs to bed.

She was indeed a bewitching creature. George Grand was proud of her, and proud, too, of the sensation she had created in society. All fashion tumbled over itself to pay her homage. And George was gratified.

Chapter Two

I

"Never," declared Benjamin Disraeli one day when giving friendly advice to a young Tory, "never in society ask who wrote the *Letters of Junius* or on any account inquire on which side of the Banqueting Hall Charles I was beheaded, for if you do you will be voted as a bore and that is—well, something dreadful."

These *Letters* to which Lord Beaconsfield referred, and which were still being so much discussed in his day, had created a tremendous amount of excitement when, in the reign of George III, they first appeared in the public press. Signed with various pseudonyms but especially that of Junius, these caustic satirical letters of political reproof and criticism "shot poisoned barbs at the highest in the land."

They were the work of Philip Francis, a brilliant young man employed as clerk in the War Office, but for years their authorship remained a matter of dialectical dispute. Indeed, the identity of Junius was still veiled in secrecy when, nominated for a seat in the recently formed Council to the Governor-General of India by Lord North, Francis sailed for Calcutta in the *Ashburnham*. He was accompanied by General Clavering and Colonel Monson, his newly appointed colleagues in the Council, both of whom fell victims to the dire climate within a few brief years.

On October 17, 1774, the three new Councillors landed at Calcutta and set foot on shore at Chandpal Ghat. Though they withheld any official complaint, they were chagrined from the very moment of landing. Warren Hastings, who met them, had not donned a ruffled shirt in their honor, and their arrival was heralded by a mere seventeen guns instead of the royal salute of twenty-one which they had expected. In a mood of ill temper the new Councillors went to a meeting next day. From that moment Francis began his quarrels with the Governor-General, disputes which were to echo in Bengal throughout the six years of his stay there and end only with the unsuccessful impeachment of Hastings years later in England.

Though in no position to judge the many difficulties of Indian administration, Francis was bursting with terrific enthusiasm for reform of the Council. Blinded by a prodigious egoism and an excessive belief in his own ability and faculty of mind, he grossly underestimated the genius of his political opponent. With slander and libel and labored innuendo he strove to undermine the Governor-General's power. But Hastings, vigorous in his wisdom, determinedly withstood the onslaughts of his First Councillor and it took years before the bitter rancor and fiery spirit of Francis shook his refined urbanity into openly expressed bad temper.

There were times when a truce was proclaimed between these two men in their struggle for and retention of power. It was always a hollow truce, broken almost as soon as it was made. For all his brilliance, Francis allowed his political conscience to be completely overshadowed by his personal hatred of the Governor-General. Finally, it was he who had to retire from the Indian stage, in the hope of crowning this failure of his career by instigating, on charges of avarice and corruption, the impeachment of his enemy in England—a long, tragic and, in the end, fruitless impeachment

> A serpent bit Francis, that virulent Knight:
> What then? 'Twas the serpent that died of the bite.

Thus, in an epigram of two lines, Hastings once summed up the character of his bitterest opponent in India. Yet in spite of his dark temper and his excessively high opinion of himself, Francis was no political adventurer. He was the only man of ability on the Council worthy of the Governor-General's mettle.

Francis' closest associates in Calcutta, after death had deprived him of his dearest friend and brother-in-law Alexander Macrabie, were his cousin Richard Tilghman, the barrister; Gerard Ducarel, the attorney-at-law; and George Shee, writer in the service of the company. But toward men in general he showed himself haughty and aloof.

Though he joined with the gentlemen of fashion in all the social refreshments of the Settlement, he was on intimate terms with extremely few. Hastings he hated—yet dined with him regularly. With Barwell, whom we despised for being indolent and greedy, he consistently sat down at the card tables. For Impey and Hyde he had a rabid dislike yet, times without number, entertained them and accepted their hospitality. He was pleased to honor Sir Robert Chambers with his friendship and approval, but for George Grand he felt nothing but contempt. Scornfully he referred to him as "that sordid old Frenchman." A gross inaccuracy, for whatever else Grand might have been, he was neither old nor a Frenchman.

If unbending in his manner toward men, Philip Francis was charmingly attentive to all women. His manner to them was one of refined courtesy, respectful veneration, captivating playfulness, and delicately expressed sentiment. While heartily disliking husbands, he was yet able "to admire beauty and to pay his respects to an agreeable woman, even in the enemy's camp." As a result, he was always on the friendliest terms with Mrs. Hastings, Lady Impey, and Mrs. Hyde.

In addition to a tongue that could drip honeyed words when he desired feminine favors, he had a tall and handsome figure and features of classical perfection. In every respect he was *l'homme aux bonnes fortunes*. A master of gallantry who had had much success with women, he was by no means silent on the subject of his amorous intrigues. He was as vain of his conquests as of his ability in the spheres of politics and literature.

Early in life he had married Alexander Macrabie's sister. She was a gentle creature who loved him with boundless admiration. Though possessing the estimable qualities that made her a good wife and mother, she lacked the most necessary attributes to make her a successful partner in his public life and overweening ambition. She did not accompany her husband to India. Patiently in England she attended to their home and the welfare of their six children, and by each packet sent him a long and detailed account of her life and her simple cares and hopes.

For this trusting, loving, sweetly credulous woman, Francis, in spite of his many victories in the field of gallantry, ever retained a sincere affection. He called her his "dearest Mrs. Francis" and sometimes, playfully, his "dearest honesty." Upon his arrival in India, and with her image still fresh in his mind, he set down in his best clerical handwriting a number of rules for his own conduct. One of these, referring to *affaires de cœur*, forthrightly counseled discretion. But fate had other plans in store for him. In time he was to forget all about that neatly penned resolution that lay between the covers of his journal.

II

In consenting to become the wife of George François Grand Catherine had followed the dictates of her heart. Unlike most women of her time, she had not allowed her head to play a part in her decision. "I married that I might go to the ball, the opera, the promenade, and the play," Madame d'Houtetot confided to Diderot. But Catherine had not so callously looked material factors in the face. It was her father who, with Gallic forethought, had made certain that Grand should find himself in a position to offer her at least a fair measure of the vanities and luxuries of life. She had married her suitor because she loved him. In an age which held up its hands in horror at overfidelity after marriage, she was still in love with her husband months after their wedding.

For young Mrs. Grand life in Calcutta appeared in two phases only—pleasure and ennui. The affection and approbation of her husband and the many social gaieties of the Settlement formed her whole world. She was happy, not with the sophisticated happiness of a woman but with the joy of a child playing in a room full of toys. She was just sixteen and neither clever nor affected with studied wit. Indeed, Catherine was never one to wag a green tongue, as the saying went. But she was sweet and cunningly mischievous and full of intriguing fancies. To George François Grand who, above all else, desired beauty, lightness, and agreeability in women, she was completely satisfying.

So, too, Philip Francis found her. Thirty-eight years old, a man of the world and of unlimited experience in love, he succumbed like a fledgling youth to her beauty and the allure of her naïve and childlike charms. When first, at routs and balls and assemblies, he singled her out for attention, she was overawed by the favor. George Grand, too, was inordinately proud of her ability to attract so mighty a man. Avaricious and ambitious, it suited him to be on friendly terms with the senior member of the Supreme Council. One never could tell to what material benefits such an association might lead. . . . Not that he actually used Catherine as a direct lever for his ambition. Still, it was pleasing to contemplate that the honor with which she was treated by Francis indirectly placed him on the debit side of that gentleman's good books.

George Grand loved his wife. Implicitly he believed in her faithfulness to him. And quite rightly so. She was honest and sincere in her affection for him and met the Senior Councillor's blandishments with playful reserve. Mistress of fashionable flirtation, she tantalized him with her glance, yet kept him at a distance. But with each meeting Francis grew more and more enamored of her, and with well-trained gallantry laid siege to her heart.

Unaware of the rising tide of his passion, Catherine piped a tune to which he, biding his time, danced patiently, though he was racked with desire. As his ardor grew in vehemence his tactics changed. Playfulness gave way to the subtle arts of enticement. He began to soothe her youthful conceits and vanities with "soft words and pleasing outward show." He excited, intrigued, and flattered her. Timidly at first she listened to his gentle innuendos and then more boldly, for his tender courtesies fed her self-esteem and filled her with naïve pride. For all that, she did not take him seriously. To her this was a pleasant pastime, a fashionable game of social coquetry. She was childishly delighted to have as opponent in this amiable recreation so august a personage as Philip Francis. Laughter played in her eyes as, blissfully, through the iron bars of her fidelity to her husband, she kept on "teasing a tiger in mistake for a cat."

Chapter Three

March of the year 1778 heralded the arrival of boisterous northwest winds which, while cooling the air, leveled verandas to the ground. In April, with the storms still unabated and after a residence of ten months in the home of old Robert Sanderson, Grand took Catherine to Chandernagore on a visit to her sister Marie de Calnois, wife of the Chief Notary Public at the French settlement. It was a short visit but a gay and highly pleasurable one, and on their return to Calcutta the Grands for the first time went to live in a home of their own, a garden house situated in a bower of trees a short distance from the town, in Alipore Lane.

Alipore was a fashionable suburb. Here, in a forest glade, stood Belvedere, the favorite residence of the Governor-General. Bordering Hastings' compounds were the noble acres of Barwell's mansion, and not far away, in even larger and finer grounds than those that surrounded Belvedere, stood the Lodge belonging to Philip Francis.

Though ill-luck dogged him at the card tables, Grand had been prospering during the last ten months, and his garden house, with its rich red walls contrasting charmingly with the dark green of the surrounding foliage and vegetation, was a large and airy dwelling. On the lower floor there was a fine hall divided by columns, for supper parties and balls. Doors covered with green venetian blinds led from it on to a large enclosed veranda. The sleeping apartments were upstairs. George and Catherine's own private suite consisted of a large bedchamber, with mosquito-net enshrouded cots, and two dressing rooms. The inner walls and the staircase were covered with chunam, a species of oyster shell which, burned and pounded and mixed with water, formed a cement that looked almost as beautiful as marble. The whole house was lighted by candles under glass shades. The furniture was Chinese in design and very elegant, and in almost every room stood vases of heavily scented flowers and bowls of perfume.

For the upkeep of so luxurious a home the Grands employed a large staff of servants, all neatly dressed in white muslin jackets, white turbans, loose gartered trousers, and gay sashes. The jemadar, or house steward, was the head of the staff. Under his control were chamber, table and sideboard servants, a man for cleaning the shoes, another who saw to the cooling of the wines, and in addition a doorkeeper, a *houccabardar,* flambeaux bearers, palanquin bearers, and kittysol boys. A kittysol boy always accompanied Grand when he walked through the street, for it was the duty of this servant to carry an enormous paper and bamboo umbrella over his master's head to keep off the sun's rays. Other kittysol boys were employed indoors, their duty being to keep the air cool by continually waving large fans of palm leaves. As her own personal maid Catherine had a pleasant, elderly ayah named Anna Lagoorda, a voracious chewer of betel nut who chattered most amusingly while she helped her mistress dress.

Sometimes, in the morning before breakfast, Catherine went for a quiet promenade with her husband. Occasionally, too, in a palanquin, she set out on a shopping expedition to the European shops. These were the fashionable rendezvous of the idle and the gay, for here, while bargaining for all manner of dainty fripperies, one exchanged the latest tidbits of gossip. More often, however, since by nature she was indolent and strongly indisposed to activity during the early part of the day, she spent the hours before breakfast lazily amusing herself with her pets. She had a collection of tame animals and pretty birds. Her favorites were a rose-ringed parakeet with the most entertaining antics and a squirrel with beady impertinent eyes that would climb on her shoulder and peer inquisitively into her face.

At last came breakfast and the time when, robed with careless perfection in the white muslin draperies of a negligee, with a fancy cap on her head and her curls falling about her shoulders, Catherine received morning callers. Barwell came often, so did Ducarel and George Shee and Farrar, all of them, even at this unconventional hour of the day, eager to pay the prettiest tributes imaginable to the most beautiful woman in Calcutta. But her most frequent visitor was Philip Francis.

II

Full of passion, Francis lavished compliments upon the lovely Mrs. Grand. He never seemed to tire of repeating his eulogies of her numberless graces and unequaled perfections. With shining eyes and cheeks suffused with blushes she listened to his praises. Laughingly she vowed that she would have to stop her ears. But this she never did. It pleased her childish heart to be so much admired and, like a little dove, she sat preening herself before the mirror of his flattery.

Her gaiety fascinated him. Her fidelity to her husband astounded and enraged him. At last, the vehemence of his ardor outstripping his sagacity, he threw all caution to the winds and grew bold and plain in his meaning and his speech. At this her lips set in a half-angry, half-frightened line. A frown puckered her white brow. With both hands she tried to stem the tide of his eager, breathless lovemaking. In her heart she carried a tender feeling for him and it grieved her to be cruel. But, strange as it might have seemed to Francis, she loved her husband and with unshakable resolution rejected the First Councillor's entreaties.

Now he fell to agitated pleading. He had cajoled too long with indirect words and silent meaningful looks. His patience was exhausted. His desire to be her lover could brook no further delay. With fiery eloquence he hammered on the barriers of her restraint. Yet she remained adamant.

gloom of his present state of mind, however, was caused neither by the untimely death of Barwell's wife nor entirely by the miseries of the climate. Catherine was principally to blame for it. Her tenacious and determined refusal to surrender to his desire had thrown him into this all-consuming fever of despair.

Chapter Four

I

For three long years the American Colonies had been waging
their War of Independence against England and now in 1778,
France, anxious to pit her strength against her old enemy, decided to throw in her lot with them. No sooner did this news
reach British India than troops were sent to capture Chandernagore, headquarters of French administrative power in Bengal.
Monsieur Pierre Werlée, the old Capitaine du Port and Catherine's father, was taken prisoner of war. Fortunately for him,
for he was in very bad health, his legs being swollen to such
enormous size that he could scarcely walk fifty yards, he was not
immured in the Calcutta jail. Influential friends in the British
settlement, inspired by Catherine and George Grand, intervened
on his behalf, and he was allowed to proceed to Balasore on pa-
role. Monsieur de Calnois, his son-in-law, was also treated generously, and was granted permission to remain at Chandernagore
and retain his office as Notary Public.

As prisoner to Calcutta came gallant Monsieur Chevalier, but
Hastings, ever a generous opponent and remembering how often
he had enjoyed the hospitality of Ghyretti House, soon allowed
the French governor to return to France by a Danish ship. Francis and his ardent supporter Wheler were greatly incensed by
this noble-hearted gesture and a fierce quarrel ensued in the
Council Chamber. The wordy battle, however, did not prevent
Francis from inviting the Governor-General to a great ball at
his Lodge at Alipore on November 23rd. On that night Philip
Francis played host at one of the outstanding social events of the
season. To his spacious Lodge, illuminated by scores of candles
under glass shades, came all the rich, the gay, and the fair of

the settlement, glittering with gold and silver lace, shimmering with silks and precious stones. Mrs. Hastings, conspicuously dressed as usual and covered with splendid ornaments, arrived with the Governor-General; Lady Impey accompanied the Chief Justice, Sir Elijah. Sir Robert and Lady Chambers, Mr. and Mrs. Hyde, Major Palmer and Major Gall, George Shee, Gerard Ducarel, and Mr. and Mrs. George François Grand—they were all there. And a host of other guests besides: young ladies in search of husbands; married ladies anxious for lovers; artillery officers in full uniform; young subalterns; affluent merchants; and a fair sprinkling of writers in the service of John Company.

The hall was splendidly decorated, the music ravishing. Wit flew from tongue to tongue and laughter filled the air. . . . Suddenly the band struck up an elegant quadrille, and ladies were led out to dance in order of their social position. The quadrille passed through its many phases—*chassez à la droite,* turn your partner, *glissez,* back to back. The rustle of silken gowns whispered like a breeze playing among autumn's fallen leaves. . . . Then the music stopped, but soon it began again with the jolly lilt of a country dance. . . . Dancing continued until midnight when a grand supper was served—soups and huge turkeys, geese, hams and beefs, legs of pickled pork and curries, puddings, jellies, wines and beers. A host of servants, as many as two to each guest, were in attendance. Kittysol boys stood behind each chair, moving great palm-leaf fans back and forth in an attempt to cool the stifling air. . . . No sooner was supper over than, with renewed vigor, dancing began again and till the small hours of the morning the band played on through its repertoire of reels and *cotillons,* of country dances, graceful waltzes, and dignified quadrilles.

All through that gay and brilliant night, Philip Francis, in stolen moments, whispered his love into the ears of Catherine Grand. He was drunk with desire for her, and she, all smiles and blushes, had grown a little drunk, too, with the wine of his pleadings and his flattery. Eyes slyly watching were quick to notice the marked attentions he showered on her that night.

But George Grand, living in the smug satisfaction of his fool's paradise of ownership, went on gaily and clumsily treading endless measures.

The evening's entertainment drew to a close. In twos and threes the guests departed. At last they were all gone and Philip Francis stood alone in his great hall. Restlessly he paced the empty floor of the ballroom. He was on tenterhooks; this game with Catherine was getting on his nerves. He was suffering acutely, for never before had he desired a woman as he now desired her. . . . She was so serene. . . . How much longer must he coax and implore and grovel at her feet! . . . Exquisite Catherine. She was divine! . . . What was it that made her withstand his vehemence with such spirit? Was it virtue or principle? She was a woman first and such moral excellence and chastity were unbelievable. . . . Unbelievable? . . . Yet, had she not this very night soothed the fever of his desire with languishing glances from her melting eyes?

Suddenly Philip Francis stood quite still. His brow was wrinkled in deep thought. He was breathing rapidly. Then in a flash the expression of his whole face changed. His eyes softened. A smile played upon his lips.

Slowly he climbed the staircase to his dressing room. He opened his journal. In his neat, careful, copyist's handwriting he wrote down the date—November 24th. After a moment's hesitation he set down beside it three Latin words: *"Omnia vincit amor"*—love overcomes all things. His eyes were shining triumphantly. He had thought of a plan.

II

With great secrecy during the days that followed Francis busied himself perfecting his scheme. He was a diplomat and diplomatically he gathered and marshaled a number of useful facts. . . . Grand was frequently absent from home in the evenings, supping and gaming either at Barwell's Lodge or at some club in town. On these occasions Catherine remained at home alone; at least, alone in the sense that she received no company. But the house and compound bristled with servants. The doorkeeper locked the front door and kept the key on his person. On the night of December 7th, Mr. and Mrs. Grand were going to a ball. The following evening Grand was going out alone, to sup with Le Gallais and a host of male friends at a club in town.

Francis had all these facts at his fingertips and, like a good chess player, carefully thought out his moves. One man only did he take into his confidence—George Shee, his closest friend in Calcutta. At first Shee was strongly opposed to the whole project. He tried his best to dissuade his friend; the planned escapade seemed to him extremely impolitic. But Francis, in a fever of impatience and desire, spurned all common sense arguments and in the end Shee capitulated. It was to his house, situated near Ducarel's and not far from Grand's, that Francis brought a dark suit and a black coat, for such garments "made one less liable to be seen at night." It was in his compound, too, that a native carpenter constructed a stout bamboo ladder for Francis, rung by rung. . . .

At about ten o'clock on the evening of December 8th, Philip Francis arrived at Shee's house. He came quite alone, unaccompanied even by palanquin bearers. When a little while later he left the house again, he was dressed in deepest black. He was carrying the bamboo ladder over his shoulder.

For some minutes after he had gone, George Shee sat brooding in his chair. Then a great restlessness took possession of him. What if Grand came home at an unexpectedly early hour? The consequences to his friend would be horrible, horrible and dangerous. Francis must be protected at all costs. Racked with worry and anxiety, Shee slipped out of his house and was swallowed up by the shadows of the night.

III

George François Grand left his home in an extraordinarily good mood soon after nine o'clock that night. As he swayed along the Alipore Road in his palanquin on his way to spend convivial hours with his friends in town, he felt pleasantly contented. He had done rather well for himself. Life was treating him kindly. He was very proud of the social footing he had gained in Calcutta, and there was every indication, too, that quite soon there would be a substantial improvement in his material state. What more could a man desire? . . . Catherine. . . . For a moment he thought happily of Catherine. He was indeed fortunate in possessing so virtuous and beautiful a wife.

Left alone to amuse herself as best she could, Catherine sat upstairs chatting with her ayah. At ten o'clock, Anna Lagoorda said: "Will Madame not undress and go to bed now?"

"No," said Catherine, pouting like a little girl. "No, Nanajee, I am not tired. Mr. Grand will be back at eleven o'clock and until that time I shall sit up."

They talked together for a little while longer. Then the ayah asked leave of her mistress to go and bring some betel nut. As she was going down the stairs Catherine called from the open door of her room: "Nana-jee, please fetch a whole candle."

A quarter of an hour later Anna Lagoorda came upstairs again, carrying her betel nut and a whole candle. When she tried to enter her mistress's room, however, she found that the door was locked. "Madame," she called, "Madame, it is I, Nana-jee." She received no reply.

Thinking her mistress was either frightened or angry because she had stayed away for a quarter of an hour, she hurried downstairs to seek the advice of one of the other servants. She went to Meerun's room—Meerun, one of the table servants—and told him what had taken place. They stood talking for a while and then Meerun went out into the compound. Suddenly his eyes fell on a ladder, a bamboo ladder which stood against the wall. Now what was that thing doing there against the wall at this time of night, he wondered? He called the jemadar, the chief of the servants. The jemadar, too, was greatly perplexed by that mysterious ladder—so were all the household, who now gathered round to examine it.

At this moment Philip Francis came out of the house. "Give me the ladder," he said.

"What business have you here?" asked the jemadar sharply.

"Give me the ladder," Francis repeated. "Don't you know me?"

"I do," came the prompt reply. "You are Mr. Francis."

"Yes, I am the Burra Sahib. Now give me the ladder and I will give you money." Invitingly Francis jingled the coins in his pocket. "I will give you money and make you great men," he added.

The jemadar remained obdurate. "My master is not at home and what have you come to do here?" he demanded. With that he and his assistants seized the First Councillor. "Run with all haste to our master and acquaint him with what has taken place," the jemadar said to a messenger, while his companions were endeavoring to carry Francis into the house by force. "Run! Run!"

Francis struggled valiantly for a time, then, feeling himself powerless, he put his fingers to his mouth and whistled several times, shrilly and piercingly.

Only with infinite trouble and after a breathless tussle did the servants at last manage to get him into the house. Roughly they forced him into a chair. When he looked up he saw Catherine standing at the top of the staircase. She held a lighted candle in her hand. Tears were streaming down her face. "What have you done!" she cried. "What have you done!" Then: "Jemadar, let him go," she called.

The jemadar eyed her sternly. "Madame," he answered, "I will not hear you. I have already sent a messenger to acquaint my master with what has happened here tonight."

Catherine began to plead, but the jemadar remained unmoved.

"It is of no avail, my dear," Francis said at last. "I beg you to go to your room." She turned away. She was weeping silently, like a heartbroken child.

Meanwhile at the sound of those shrill whistles that had echoed through the night, George Shee had rushed across to Ducarel's house, crying loudly: "Francis is being murdered in Grand's house. Come along, there is no time to lose." Out of his bed jumped dwarfish Ducarel. He called to his friend Shore, who slept in a room close by. Without stopping to dress, they followed Shee, Ducarel lumbering along on his short fat legs, brandishing his sword. Across the road they went and over the compound wall. They burst noisily into the hall where, guarded by a small band of servants and with the jemadar holding him down in a chair, sat Philip Francis. And in this instant confusion became confounded. . . .

But what of Grand? In the middle of a dinner that he was enjoying enormously, he was told the news that Francis had been caught in his house. At the messenger's ominous words he leaped from the table like a stone shot from a sling. Full of vengeance and misery, he rushed to the home of Major Palmer, borrowed that gentleman's sword and, requesting his good friend to accompany him, hastened with all speed to the red brick house in Alipore Lane. But when, followed closely by Major Palmer, he rushed into the hall of his house sword in hand, there was no First Councillor to be seen anywhere. During the heated melee, and in the darkness and general disorder that had ensued on the arrival of his rescuers, Francis had made good his escape. In the chair so recently occupied by the First Councillor sat George Shee, forcefully held as hostage by the faithful jemadar. Around him, begging for his release, stood Ducarel and Shore and two other neighbors, Keeble and Archdekin, who had been attracted by the disturbance.

Explanations followed; the jemadar told his story; Shee was released. Almost immediately afterward, beside himself with

sorrow, anger, and self-pity, and determinedly refusing to see
Catherine, George Grand left his own house to spend the re-
maining hours of that fateful night in town with his friend
Major Palmer.

IV

Francis had gotten safely home. Before preparing for bed he
seated himself at his desk to jot down the happenings of the
day in his journal. First he wrote the date. It was December 8th.
Then followed a few lines concerning his public affairs. Finally,
with the single forceful sentence: "At night the *diable à quatre*
at the house of G. F. Grand, Esqr.," he concluded the entry.

The devil to pay. A neat way for Francis to sum up a situation which for Catherine was nothing short of tragedy. Up in
her room in the red brick garden house, her head pillowed on
her folded arms, she sat weeping piteously. Unspeakable sorrow
filled her heart. To think that her dear George should have gone
off without so much as a word to her! It was unbelievable!
Without so much as a word! Oh, indeed, indeed, she understood
his anger. It was just and right. If only he had allowed her to
explain. She had been foolish and indiscreet. But she was innocent—innocent of everything but vanity and coquetry. . . .
She had had not even the slightest advance knowledge of Francis' visit. He had crept upon her unexpectedly, like a thief. She
had been afraid at first. Then courage had come to her. With
angry words she had repulsed and rejected his violent pleadings
and, in deep mortification, he had left her. . . . If only George
would let her explain, then surely, since he loved her, he would
understand and forgive her. . . . Before her tear-dimmed eyes
passed visions of the happy times she had spent with her husband. She was helpless in her misery. Her brain, her whole being,
was numbed and chilled.

As if she were a small child, her ayah undressed her and
helped her into bed. There, in misery, she lay motionless. At
last, utterly wearied, she fell asleep.

George Grand did not sleep that night. Bowed down with grief he sat in a chair in Major Palmer's house, awaiting the morning. At the first sign of dawn he sent a note of challenge to the undoer of his happiness.

> SIR,
> The steps you took to dishonour me last night bind me to demand that satisfaction which is alone open to me. If, notwithstanding your unprincipled character, you have yet one spark of honour left, you will not refuse me a meeting tomorrow morning. The time, place and weapons I leave to your choice and will acquaint you that I shall bring with me a second.
>
> I am, Sir,
Your humble servant,
G. F. GRAND.

Impatiently he awaited the reply to his demand. At last it came; a short laconic note.

> SIR,
> You are certainly under some gross deception, which I am unable to account for. Having never injured you, I know not for what reason I should give you satisfaction. I must, therefore, decline your request and am,
>
> Sir,
Your most obedient humble servant,
P. FRANCIS.

Thrown completely off balance by this arrogant missive, Grand raved and fumed. He was quite beyond himself in the violence of his passion. At last he grew calm again. Francis had impudently refused to grant him satisfaction according to a gentleman's code of honor. Very well then, he would take his grievance to a court of law. He would justify himself in the eyes of established authority. As for Francis, he would ruin that gay Lothario morally, socially, politically, and financially. Financially? That word set up a new train of thought. George

François Grand's blood once again stirred in his veins. Suddenly, though bowed down with grief by the tragedy that had shattered his domestic bliss, he saw that it was possible for even the darkest cloud to have a silver lining. Straightway then he went about the business of setting legal machinery in motion. On a plea of trespass and "the loss of the help, solace, affection, comfort and council of his wife," he instructed his attorney to sue Philip Francis for damages. Meanwhile, too, having sent for his sister- and brother-in-law, Monsieur and Madame de Calnois, to come to Calcutta, he returned to his own home to await their arrival. Still he refused to see Catherine. While he occupied the lower rooms of the house, he insisted upon her remaining in the upper portion.

Grand managed his affairs with the prudence and discretion of a skilled politician. Quite firmly, he had made up his mind to heal the wounds of his deep affliction with several lacs of rupees from the coffers of Philip Francis.

V

M. and Mme. de Calnois arrived. In her room in the upper part of the house, Catherine told them her story. In the hall downstairs, George told his. Catherine had broken his heart, he declared miserably. He was shattered in mind and body. She had ruined his social position and his office. He could never again live with her as his wife. Indeed, he would not even remain under the same roof with her. They must take her back with them to Chandernagore, to live in their home and under their protection. Fate had dealt him a dastardly blow. Nevertheless he was prepared to show himself generous to Catherine. He would "contribute what was requisite for her support," and this over and above "the monthly allowance which he chose to allot to her own disposal." So he sealed Catherine's destiny. Before sending her from his home, but only after pitiful entreaties, he granted her an interview. It lasted three hours.

She told him quite simply the truth of her association with Philip Francis and of the arts he had used to force her to surrender her chastity. She confessed to coquetry and the flattery that had touched her heart as a result of the august First Councillor's gallantry and attention. That he had ever been her successful lover or that she had been a party to his nocturnal visit, she emphatically denied. She wept and pleaded. "I implore you to believe me, George," she entreated, clinging to his hands. "I am innocent. Oh, my dear, if you would only believe me!"

It would have been easy enough to succumb to her pleading, but George Grand stood firm as a rock. He was filled with righteous indignation, and he deliberately thrust all that had been dear and sacred to him behind the barriers of his injured self-esteem, his blind contempt. "It is useless, Catherine," he said bitterly. "I no longer trust you."

"Have you no pity for my sufferings?" she asked. "Will you not try to understand? I love you, George. Only you. You are my husband."

He looked at her sternly, she whom once he had regarded with such tender affection, and answered coldly: "Our love has been wounded unto death. All these poignant lamentations are useless. Utterly useless, madam." She stared at him miserably, with pain in her eyes. She felt as if she were choking. Her hands went up to her throat. "But I forgive you and pity you from my heart," he added pompously. "From the depths of my heart."

So, "with a sorrow approaching to distraction," as Grand wrote in his *Narrative* years later, they parted. Catherine went to live with her sister Marie de Calnois at Chandernagore.

Chapter Five

I

The events of the night of December 8th did not long remain private property. Very soon a hurricane of gossip and tittle-tattle swept Calcutta, creating a great stir in every boudoir, drawing room, and tavern in the settlement. Nothing else was talked about. Those who hated Francis attacked him bitterly. The prudes loudly cried out their support for the injured Grand. But a great proportion of the inhabitants—particularly the male element—sympathized with Catherine, the much tempted and misunderstood child wife, eating out her heart in Chandernagore. She was more sinned against than sinning, they said. One could feel only compassion and pity for her. Some of the gilded youth even went so far as to dub Grand a "thoroughly odious fellow," while Francis they almost invariably dressed in the character of the Evil Seducer of Innocence.

Hastings and Barwell immediately sent the complete story of the outrage to the Court of Directors in England. Fortunately for Francis, he was warned of this in time and was able to write to Lord North himself before the Governor-General's papers left India, a stroke of luck for Francis and one that placed him at a great advantage. He was furious with the Governor-General and Barwell, and in a sense quite justifiably so, for neither of these gentlemen was in a position to throw stones for lapses of moral rectitude. Hastings had lived with Mrs. Imhoff for several years before she became his wife, and in Calcutta's memory Barwell's *affaire galante* with Sarah Bonner was still remarkably green. In Wheler's behavior, however, Francis found great consolation. Most handsomely, in the midst of the clamors of the settlement, did Wheler conduct himself toward his friend and political colleague. And Philip Francis was deeply touched by his wife's understanding. In a letter that in matter, style, and literary composition was a feat of genius, he told her of his "platonic" regard for Catherine. For Mrs. Grand, he declared, his feelings were purely those of friendship and deep sympathy for a beautiful child married to an "ugly old sordid Frenchman." Mrs. Francis, simple and credulous, believed him. . . .

At dinners, balls, and on the Race Course, Calcutta gossips chattered on. Through the swirling mass of sympathy and censure flowed a swift river of witticisms. A popular *jeu de mots,* one among the many that were being bandied about, was this, composed and circulated in the clubs by Colonel Ironside:

> Psha! What a fuss, twixt *Shee* and twixt her!
> What abuse of a dear little creature,
> A *Grand* and a mighty affair to be sure,
> Just to give a light *Philip* (fillip) to nature.
> How can you, ye prudes, blame a luscious young wench,
> Who so fond is of love and romances,
> Whose customs and manners are *tout à fait* French,
> For admiring whatever from *France-is!* . . .

Meanwhile, with but little delay, the machinery of the law had been set in motion. Grand succeeded in persuading his solicitor to bring an action against the First Councillor and put his case with Mr. Newman. Served with the writ, Francis placed his defense in the hands of his close friend and cousin, Richard Tilghman.

But now there occurred a most unfortunate hitch in the proceedings. Grand's chief witness, George Shee, on whose evidence, as the plaintiff declared, "every hope of crimination rested," could not be found. The case kept coming on before the Court and again and again had to be postponed because of Shee's nonappearance. That gentleman, on the advice of his "good patron" Philip Francis, had gone into hiding. He was nowhere to be found—though he was, in fact, at Purnea. Eventually, however, it was deemed advisable for him to return to Calcutta and the case was at last brought before the Supreme Court.

II

The courthouse that day was packed with fashionable Calcutta society. With breathless expectation the arrival of the judges was awaited. At last they came, marching in solemn procession—Chief Justice Sir Elijah Impey at the head, robed in red, followed by Sir Robert Chambers and Mr. Justice Hyde. In a loud voice the marshal of the court called out the nature of the proceedings: "George François Grand, Esq., in the Company's services, *versus* Philip Francis, Esq., Councillor of the Presidency of Fort William in Bengal. . . . An action for criminal conversation of the wife of the plaintiff, etc. . . . The damages alleged to be fifteen hundred thousand *sicca* rupees."

The trial had commenced.

For two months it passed through its various stages. At the end of that time the only substantial facts proved against Francis were that he had frequently visited Grand's house and that, on the night of December 8th, he had deliberately gone there knowing full well that the master was absent from home. Trespass was conclusively proved on the testimony of Shee, Ducarel, and Grand's servants. On no evidence, however, was criminal intercourse established. "The evidence," declared Sir Robert Chambers, "appears to me to fall short of what is ordinarily considered as proof of any fact and especially of any crime," and, therefore, since no criminality had been proved, he was fully of the opinion that the charge in the suit had failed.

Mr. Justice Hyde, suffering from moral righteousness and staunchly opposed to any form of "gallantry in the bedchamber," determinedly held the opinion that damages of one hundred thousand *sicca* rupees should be given to the plaintiff.

Finally, on March 6th, Chief Justice Sir Elijah Impey rose to pronounce judgment. It was true, declared his Lordship, that adultery had not been proved, but since the plaintiff had been grievously wronged by the defendant entering his wife's apartments at night and thus destroying her reputation, judgment was for the plaintiff with compensating damages of fifty thousand *sicca* rupees.

"Fifty thousand *sicca* rupees," his Lordship added with fine elaboration, "are equal to five thousand one hundred and nine pounds, two shillings and eleven pence sterling, reckoning according to the weight and fineness of the silver."

That night, with a single line in his diary, Francis recorded his defeat. "March 6: Judgment against me in the Supreme Court." He had lost a great sum of money and a good deal of prestige. But he still had the tender trust and affection of his wife in distant England, and his desire for the woman he had so deeply wronged in India was as ardent and pressing as ever. . . .

With Francis' rupees in his pocket and having signed his name to a paper declaring himself "fully satisfied, contented and paid," Grand looked around for new worlds to conquer. A week after his victory in the Supreme Court, he filed an action for trespass and housebreaking against George Shee. This time, alas, the fruits of conquest were bitterly disappointing. Judgment was pronounced for "one rupee damages and one rupee costs."

III

The Grand-Francis *cause célèbre* more than ever embittered Francis against Hastings, Impey, and Hyde. Though outwardly he maintained friendly social relations with them, inwardly his whole being was afire with anger and resentment. He talked with them at the Harmonic Tavern, he dined with Mr. and Mrs. Hastings, he entertained them at his house, he frequented the home of the Chief Justice. But while in public he was professing such great respect for Sir Elijah, in private he was intriguing to displace him from office in favor of Sir Robert Chambers, who was his friend politically as well as socially. Chambers, he considered, had shown himself "a wise and upright judge" during the trial. Not like Hyde with his fulsome moral self-righteousness. For Hyde he felt particular enmity and during the ensuing year diligently but secretly strove to get him removed from the Bench of the Supreme Court.

Francis could be a very good friend. He was, however, a much better hater. The seeds of his resentment against the Governor-General and the Chief Justice, sown when he first arrived in India, were fostered by the Grand case. Years later, they bore their fruits when he influenced the impeachment of both Hastings and Impey before the House of Lords in England.

It was none too pleasant for the self-important George Grand that Philip Francis still retained his high position in the Supreme Council. In addition, Calcutta's sympathies were on the whole very definitely anti-Grand, for though he had not entirely ruined his wife's reputation by taking his domestic troubles to a court of law, it was held that he had most abominably and unmercifully played with her fair name. Under these circumstances kind friends advised him to "change the air," and quite suddenly he discovered that "his health had been sensibly affected" by the trials and tribulations and sorrows of the past months. With the aid of influential intimates—Hastings and Barwell were still kindly disposed toward him—he secured the position of Head Commercial Assistant to the Indigo Factory at Patna. To Patna then he went, just a month after his victory in the Supreme Court. Scarcely had the noise of his departure died down when Francis, with "thoughts full of matters amatory," made his first trip up the river to Chandernagore.

Chapter Six

I

To Catherine, so full of the desire for happiness, for love and gaiety, the shock of being rejected and forsaken by George, for whom she had felt the tenderest affection, was unbearable and soul-shattering. During the first weeks after her return to Chandernagore with her sister Marie, she abandoned herself unrestrainedly to tears and heartache. It seemed to her as if all the loveliness had faded forever out of her life. Then suddenly a fresh bewilderment shook her out of her black despair. News had come from Calcutta that Grand was determined to take the whole dreadful affair to a court of law. Hither and thither, like the pendulum of a clock, swung Catherine's strained feelings. It was unbelievable that George should wish to hurt her even more deeply than he had already done, and day by day the confusion of her mind waxed till it fermented into boiling anger and resentment.

But at last the case ended, and with its termination her emotions gradually cooled down, leaving her nothing but a feeling of utter weariness. Life, she felt, had passed her by. At this time Catherine was just seventeen. Caprice and weakness had made her the type of woman created solely for happiness. Believing herself now forever divorced from the joys she cherished, she gave herself up completely to devastating ennui.

But if George François Grand had spurned and rejected her, she was forgotten neither by the world of Calcutta nor by Philip Francis. All through the months before and during the trial Francis' longing for her remained unallayed. And it was her oval face framed in pale gold curls, her soft sensuous mouth, her blue eyes dark-lashed and velvety, her countless charms that drew him up the river to Chandernagore. The power of her spell was as intense as ever. On seeing her again he made this cryptic entry in his diary: "*Ut vidi, ut perii*"—as I saw, so I died. . . .

Once again he resumed his romantic courtship, his eloquent pleadings and his blandishments. But Catherine, numbed by the sufferings of the past months, refused to listen to his passionate entreaties. In his diary he bemoaned her coldness in short Latin, French, and Italian quotations. "*O cara Phillide, rendi me il cor,*" he wrote at Chandernagore in August. Her resolute rejection of his suit was breaking his heart.

Philip Francis, however, was determined to have his way. If he could not conquer her with passion, he would win her by gentleness. The more she checked him, the more solicitously tender did he become. In visit upon visit he poured the phial of his eloquence into her ears, till at last it seemed to him that he did read in her eyes the faintest glimmer of response.

By warming her chilled heart and soothing her injured vanity his flattery was doing its work. Soon she was no longer able to resist the strength of his romantic lovemaking. Her listlessness gave place to playful tenderness. Then one day as he stood smiling down at her, he seemed suddenly handsomer than ever she had imagined, and very great indeed. His face was close to hers, his voice low and intense. When his lips sought hers she did not turn away her head.

That day at Chandernagore, Catherine Grand, who for three long months had withstood the eloquence of Philip Francis' lovemaking, finally consented to pass into his "protection." He promised her all the delights for which she yearned—riches, love, and comfort. In return she gave him, gladly and willingly, the gay affection of her youth and her incomparable beauty.

II

On his arrival in Calcutta Francis had carefully noted down in his journal a number of "Hints for my Own Conduct." In all there were seventeen of these acutely judicious guiding principles to discreet behavior. Number twelve, beginning: "If certain connections be formed, to keep at a distance," obviously referred to just such an intrigue as this with Catherine. Unfortunately, with the years the power of this axiom had grown rather weak. Francis, hearing it now only as a faintly whispered admonition, interpreted it in a manner best suited to his present mood and the desire which prompted him to offer his "protection" to the neglected and rejected wife of George François Grand. Recognizing the wisdom of not transgressing beyond certain bounds of public propriety of conduct, he did not take Catherine under his own roof. His home in Calcutta, situated behind the Playhouse, retained for the time being its purely bachelor character. So did the Lodge at Alipore, which he sold a few months later for 30,000 rupees. It was at Hooghly, a mile or two beyond Chinsurah, which again was above Chandernagore, that he established Catherine in the elegant modern villa belonging to his cousin Major Phil Baggs.

Major Baggs had recently arrived in India. His landing at Calcutta had taken place on the very day of the escapade at Grand's house. He was a grim-countenanced man with little appeal to women. His notoriety rested on his dueling prowess and his activity at the gaming tables. Francis knew that he could find no better watchdog for his enchanting Catherine than this fire-eating Irishman and sent her to live at Major Baggs's villa at Hooghly, ostensibly under that gentleman's pugnacious chaperonage.

Though discretion decreed that the First Councillor should not attend Mrs. Grand "abroad," he saw to it that she was neither isolated in her retreat nor banished from the delights of fashionable society. Sir Robert and Lady Chambers and Mr. Wheler, the very cream of Calcutta bon ton, were frequent visitors at Hooghly. Their openly expressed friendship imbued the liaison with the virtue of respectability. Indeed, since in a sense the Hooghly villa had become his home, Francis did most of his entertaining there and at regular intervals all his friends came up the river to dinner, ball, or rout.

Francis went to Calcutta only for the urgent business of Council meetings. No sooner was this accomplished than with all haste he hurried back to Catherine who, in the milk-white villa, awaited his return with the utmost impatience. For the First Councillor, the ablest as well as the most fiery of men in public life, the house at Hooghly became a haven of peace. Here he tried to forget his quarrels with Hastings and, throwing aside the cares of his political position, became the eloquent lover, all amiability and honeyed charm. On Catherine he lavished the passion and tenderness of his ardent disposition. He spoiled and adored her and showered her with gifts. Though mentally she was no match for a man of his brilliance, her naïvetés filled him with delight. She never bored him for an instant. To him she was ever an intriguing and exciting combination of woman, dryad, child, and toy.

Those were lotus-eating days for Catherine. She was queen of a beautiful idyll, and played her part contentedly and happily. She was so gay, so tender and endearing, that Francis found her an anodyne for the stress of his embittered public life. Whenever, on his return from Calcutta, she came to welcome him, gowned in flowered silk with knots of blue ribbon on her shoulders to match the color of her eyes, she appeared to him the very embodiment of grace and beauty. It seemed to him that he would never grow tired of looking at her. Whether she sat playing with her pets or gravely sewing at her embroidery, she was always enchanting to watch. Best of all he liked those evenings they spent together alone, when, indolently reclining on a couch, she prattled happy as a child, while he sat beside her smoking his long-tubed hookah. Often in the years that followed he remembered these hours with Catherine, spent in the peace and contentment of a room filled with the scent of tuberoses, of Indian stocks and oleanders in tall vases.

During all this last half of the year 1779, Francis' trips up the river from Calcutta were numerous and frequent. His diary is full of references to the glorious days passed in the Hooghly paradise, where he stayed as long as he could, visiting Calcutta only when absolutely necessary for the purpose of attending Council meetings. In his newfound happiness there was little room in his thoughts for a romantic image of his good and faithful wife in England. She felt his neglect bitterly. "I was but too sure separation would make a great alteration in your affection, and indeed I am sorry to say, I fear it has—a very great one indeed," she wrote pathetically in a letter to him at this time. Francis was assailed by sharp twinges of conscience on receipt of this letter and immediately wrote to his "dearest Mrs. Francis" from Hooghly to reassure her of his affection. He sent her, too, as a token of his respect and esteem, a gift of a magnificent pair of pearl earrings.

The Hooghly heaven had been in existence for just six months when suddenly the Court of Directors of the Honourable Company decided that the presence of the fire-eating Major Baggs in Bengal was most undesirable. They ordered his instant departure. In Hicky's *Bengal Gazette,* the first newspaper to be published in British India, the following advertisement was inserted soon after the paper first appeared on January 29, 1780: "For Sale, an elegant modern built house at Hooghly, lately inhabited by Major Baggs."

With the watchdog of his paradise so summarily dispatched from India, Francis decided to take Catherine to Calcutta. He established her under the chaperonage of Lady Chambers, a "species of chaperonage" which gave the stamp of social approval to his association with her.

III

Politically the settlement was in a mild mood. Differences between the Senior Councillor and the Governor-General had been bridged over by a truce, and Francis had promised his support to Hastings in the war which at this time he was waging against the Mahrattas near the Malabar Coast.

During this interim of harmony Barwell, whose vote up to

now had given the Governor-General a predominating position in the Council, decided to return to England. He felt quite easy in his mind at leaving India, for Francis had pledged his faith to Hastings, and the Government for once was running on oiled wheels. On February 17th he called at Francis' house in town to pay his respects to Catherine. They talked, and he discovered that, tentatively, she had been toying with the idea of going to live in France with some of her father's relations. Barwell proposed that she secure a passage in the *Swallow,* the ship which was taking him to England within a few weeks. This gallant suggestion met with Philip Francis' flat refusal. He disliked Barwell intensely and had not the slightest intention of exposing Catherine to the blandishments of a man whom he considered grossly profligate, depraved, and cunning. The very thought of her in the same ship as Barwell alarmed him. One might as well deliberately coop a sheep and a wolf together in the same pen. Besides, there would be time enough to decide Catherine's fate if ever he should find it impossible to continue the tenure of his office on the Council of Bengal. Meantime she must stay in India and remain under his protection.

A fortnight later Barwell called again—"to take his leave with a fine palavering speech," Francis noted down in his diary that night, in open contempt of his departing colleague.

No sooner was Barwell gone than the snake of discord once again raised its head in the Council Chamber. Not only did Francis reopen his attack on the power of the Governor-General with renewed vigor, but now, too, he suddenly and most vehemently opposed the conduct of the Mahratta war to which, before Barwell's departure, he had promised his support. Political matters came to a head in August as the direct result of a minute penned by Hastings and sent to Francis on the night before a Council meeting. Though no doubt justifiable, Hastings minute was provocative in the extreme. "I did hope," ran one paragraph of the document, "that the intimation conveyed in my last minute would have awakened in Mr. Francis's breast, if it were susceptible to such sensations, a conscious-

ness of the faithless part which he was acting towards me."
"My authority of the opinions I have declared concerning Mr.
Francis," stated another portion, "depends on facts which have
passed within my knowledge. I judge of his public conduct
by my experience of his private, which I have found void of
truth and honour. . . ." To such assertions there could be but
one answer from Francis, an answer which Hastings expected
and for which he was fully prepared.

Hastings had carried the idea of this challenging minute in
his mind for some weeks, but as Francis was then in bed suffering with fever, he had decided to wait for the First Councillor's
recovery before handing him the accusing document. Meanwhile, clearly foreseeing the possible consequences, he had arranged for his "dearest Marian" to be safely out of the way.
On August 4th, he had gone up the river to Sooksagur with
the "Lady Governess" and on his return to Calcutta ten days
later persuaded her to remain at Chinsurah as guest of the Governor's wife. On the night of his arrival he sent the provocative
minute to Francis, who had completely recovered by now.
Colonel Watson, Chief Engineer at Fort William, a gentleman
bitterly opposed to the Governor-General, happened to be
dining with the First Councillor on the following evening, and
agreed to act as his second. Hastings secured Colonel Pearse,
Commandant of Artillery, to perform the same service for him,
and a meeting was arranged for the early morning of August
17th.

Chapter Seven

I

One outside spectator only was fortunate enough to see the most famous duel ever fought in India. An old Hindu woman, passing on her way that early morning, stopped to watch the strange behavior of the four white sahibs. She laughed uproariously at what seemed to her the maddest and most diverting game she had ever seen played in the forest near Belvedere.

The whole matter was wrapped in such profound secrecy that no one in Calcutta aside from the two participants and their seconds was aware of the encounter, which had been fixed to take place near the road opposite Alipore and close to Belvedere. On the night before the duel, while Catherine slept in peace, oblivious of the sword of Damocles that hung suspended above her lover's head, Francis spent long hours burning papers, writing letters, and setting his private and public business in order.

"I am forced into the field," he confided to Wheler in a short farewell missive, "by such insults as I think no degree of resentment nor any sense of injury, however unjust, will warrant among gentlemen. . . . Defend my memory and leave this country, as soon as you can, to its own Fate. . . . Yours while I still live," he concluded mournfully.

At half-past five the next morning, when Hastings and his second reached the appointed meeting place, Francis and Watson had already arrived. Viewed at this hour, the spot previously chosen appeared extremely unsuitable. Lying close to the main road along which, in the early morning, riders frequently passed, it was obviously much too open to the public gaze. Unanimously, therefore, it was deemed advisable to select a more sheltered place for the encounter, among the trees near the Lodge once occupied by Barwell. Finally a dry and secluded spot was discovered. The pistols were loaded. Pearse handed one to Hastings, and Watson the other to Francis.

"Now, gentlemen," said Colonel Pearse in a businesslike tone of voice, "will you kindly fix your distance, for it is the duty of the seconds to pace it off accurately."

"Distance?" repeated Francis. "I regret that I am unacquainted with these matters, for I have never fired a pistol in my life."

"And I, sir," Mr. Hastings asserted, "do not recollect having myself ever fired a pistol above once or twice."

"Very well then," said the practical Watson, "I recommend fourteen paces."

"Fourteen paces?" retorted Hastings in a sudden bellicose humor. "That seems to me a very great distance for pistols."

"Indeed, sir, no great distance at all, I assure you," declared Colonel Pearse authoritatively.

Watson interrupted sharply. "Colonel Pearse, since both gentlemen seem unacquainted with the modes usually observed on these occasions, shall we fix the distance at fourteen paces?"

"Agreed," said Pearse with finality.

So while Pearse paced, Watson counted, and when all the preparatory business had been completed the duelists took up their positions and came to the present. Francis raised his hand but almost instantly came down to present again. Twice again he raised his hand, but each time brought it down. He had discovered, upon attempting to press the trigger, that his powder was damp. Patiently Hastings waited while the misfiring pistol was reloaded and readjusted. Then, for the fourth time, the two gentlemen took up their positions, presented, and, almost simultaneously, fired.

With a shrill sigh Francis' bullet hissed past the Governor-General's ear. The next instant Hastings' shot had found its mark, entering just below the right shoulder and lodging in the opposite side under the left. As Francis staggered and fell to the ground Hastings and Watson rushed toward him and

Pearse hurried off to call the servants and to fetch a sheet to bind the wound.

His face distorted with pain, the First Councillor whispered hoarsely: "I am a dead man. A dead man."

"Good God! I most sincerely hope not," Hastings said, frankly distressed. "Watson," he called, "Watson, run with all speed and fetch a cot or palanquin from Belvedere so that we may carry Mr. Francis to town." Then again he turned to the injured man. "Indeed I most earnestly trust all will be well," he declared, "but if anything unfortunate should happen, I shall immediately surrender myself to the sheriff."

At this juncture Pearse returned with the sheet and the Governor-General assisted him in binding up Francis' wound. Scarcely was this done when Watson arrived with a cot. It was decided to carry the wounded man on the cot to Pearse's carriage and to hurry him to town. But on the way to the vehicle the jolting over the rough path so distressed Francis, who was in great pain, that they urged him to allow them to carry him to Belvedere instead. Hastings and Pearse, meanwhile, set off for Calcutta and immediately on arrival there dispatched Dr. Campbell, the Surgeon General of the Presidency, and Dr. Francis, the Governor-General's own surgeon, to Belvedere.

The two doctors reached the injured man an hour and a half after he had been wounded. Without delay they cut out the ball lodged under his left shoulder. Later that day they bled him twice. Francis, having fortunately escaped extinction by Hasting's pistol, was now in really grave danger of being put to death by the well-intentioned but perilous treatment of his overconscientious medical attendants. For several days he suffered greatly from pain and weakness, but miraculously, and in spite of the drastic remedies to which he was subjected, he recovered and a week later was able to return to Calcutta.

The next Council meeting was marked by great civility between the Governor-General and the Senior Councillor. "Both parties behaved as became gentlemen of their high rank and station." Hastings, as he had written and told Marian, felt in a "state of perfect tranquillity." And no wonder, for once again he had scored a victory over Francis.

Vibrant with excitement, Calcutta searched in vain in the pages of Hicky's scandalous *Bengal Gazette* for an account of this stirring affair of honor between the two highest personages in the land. For once Hicky kept a discreet silence. He had too great a respect for Philip Francis. If only the tables had been turned at that meeting place near Belvedere, how gladly and how willingly would he have treated the Governor-General with ribaldry.

II

Prior to this duel, Francis had with some confidence anticipated the recall of Warren Hastings to England and his own elevation to the highest position in the Indian service. He had guardedly communicated his expectations in a letter to his wife. However, he expressed himself with so much caution that, instead of making her happy, he succeeded only in filling her with doubt and apprehension. "Your staying in India one year more is the most dreadful disappointment to me," she answered him. "What can detain you, my dear Philip? Indeed I cannot say as you, it is quite indifferent to me whether you stay or come here; it is not so to me, I can assure you, for all my happiness depends upon my seeing you. I am sorry to find it not so with you."

Francis' cherished hopes, however, were not to be realized. Soon dispatches arrived from England confirming Hastings' further tenure of the Governor-Generalship of Bengal, and Francis was left to face the unequivocal fact that his star in India was setting. In the mood of despondency that overwhelmed him during these distressing days, Catherine's natural sweetness of disposition, her serenity and innate indolence, made her a restful companion. Her grace and beauty brought him consolation. Her agreeability to one racked by the stress and storms of political life was a veritable balm. She was neither clever enough to ask leading questions nor stupid enough to offer advice. Indeed, in these troublesome days he found her "understanding very great." Out of her deep gratitude she showed him consideration and affection and in a hundred ways tried to relieve his dejection and his dark mood. Her artless attempts to make him happy were so innocent, and when her gaiety brought a smile to his lips she was as delighted as a child with her achievement. And he was deeply touched by this and by her sympathy.

III

Whatever else may be said against Philip Francis, his desire for India's welfare is unquestionable. The Francis of the Bengal period was no mere political adventurer. Though a virulent and rancorous human being, he was a brilliantly able statesman and an honest one. It is true that in his struggle against Warren Hastings he used every weapon that came to his hands, but it was because he sincerely believed the Government of India to be unprincipled and corrupt that such methods seemed justifiable to him. His honesty of purpose can perhaps best be gauged by these words of former Lord Chancellor Brougham. "Francis," he declared, "had been an Indian satrap in the most corrupt times and retired from the barbaric land, the land of pearls and gold, with a fortune so moderate that in the fiercest storms of faction no man ever for an instant dreamt of questioning the absolute purity of his administration. . . ."

After the duel with Warren Hastings a lull fell on the political battlefield of Bengal. The moods of the Governor-General and his Senior Councillor were varying and diverse. While Hastings looked forward to his renewed tenure of Government with composure and tranquillity, Francis stared the failure of his Indian career full in the face. For six long years, fighting with every instrument that came to his hand, vilifying the character of the Governor-General, stirring up public hatred against him, provoking disobedience and frustrating Hastings' authority, he had tried to establish the reforms in which he believed so ardently. It had all been in vain. He could no longer stand up against the power of Warren Hastings nor against his tenacity of purpose. At last, like Macaulay, he came to realize that "all the fruits of the tropics are not worth a pottle of Covent Garden strawberries and that a lodging up three pairs of stairs in London is better than a palace in a compound of Chowringhee."

Francis announced his intention of leaving for England to the Council and one day he gently told Catherine that their Indian idyll was over. "How long is it since we first met, Catherine?" he asked.

"I have been so happy and you have been so good and gracious to me," she answered, "that I have long ago stopped counting the weeks and months."

"You are very sweet," he said tenderly, "sweet and beautiful as a nymph out of some ancient Greek legend." He told her of his plans for her. She would accompany him on the long voyage. He would establish her in France, to which he knew she ardently desired to go. "So you see, my dear, this is not the end for us," he said. "For surely I mean to return to you. I shall come to see you in Paris, Catherine."

"In Paris? And you will love me still, Philip?"

"I shall always love you," he vowed. "How could my eyes ever behold you with apathy? You have been, and always will be, Venus to me."

But their plans to leave India together were frustrated. Early in November Francis recorded this, the last entry in his Indian diary: "Discovered at last that it is impossible to go in the Dutch ship, so resolved to take my passage in the *Fox*." It was in the "Dutch ship" that Catherine's passage was booked.

She wept bitterly at the thought of separation from him on the long voyage to Europe. He held her close to his heart, comforting her with soft words, ardent protestations, and promises of a speedy reunion. So he coaxed the smiles back into her eyes. Catherine was young and all life lay before her. She was going to France, to Paris! Soon, for so he had promised her, she would once again see her dear Philip. France, Paris, Philip! How *could* she remain sad for long?

But when the time for parting came, she could not stem her tears. "Think of me kindly," she pleaded. *"Adieu, mon ami! Adieu, adieu."*

The Dutch ship which, according to a notice in Hicky's *Bengal Gazette*, "carried home Mrs. Grand," left Diamond Harbour, forty miles down the river from Calcutta, on a December afternoon. A day later, with his cousin Richard Tilghman as fellow passenger, Philip Francis sailed from India in the *Fox*.

Chapter Eight

I

Not once since the day he had so self-righteously sent her off to Chandernagore with the De Calnoises had George Grand seen Catherine. "We remained from that moment like those who, having lived for a time in the height of happiness, have witnessed that happiness suddenly and unexpectedly interrupted by one being cut off never in this world to meet again. . . . We knew the delicacy of each other's sentiments, and never once thought of infringing that line of conduct which such a sense of feeling naturally prescribed," he wrote in his *Narrative* years later. With such noble-sounding phrases he clothed his overweening egotism and self-love. For it was these qualities in his character that had enabled him to abide so determinedly by the "eternal separation" upon which, after mature consideration, he had fixed his thoughts. Small wonder that Catherine's departure for France did not overmuch ruffle his composure and peace of mind. Pompous and vainglorious as ever, he was much too busy feathering his nest at Patna. But he was by no means satisfied with his material success. Life, he felt, most assuredly held more in store for him than a mere Head Commercial Assistantship in the factory at Patna.

Hardly was Catherine out of India than he once again took to scheming assiduously and industriously for his material advancement. His strivings to further his worldly status were indefatigable. With cunning and skill he wriggled himself into the notice of Chief Justice Sir Elijah Impey, insinuated himself into the good graces of the heads of the Government, and literally groveled at the feet of the Governor-General. By these means he eventually succeeded in attaining his desires.

83

In his inimitable style and manner James Augustus Hicky records Grand's success in his *Bengal Gazette*. "Mr. Grand who has lately been much employed in reading and digesting Milton on divorce," the account states, "will, we hear, in a few days be appointed Collector of Turhoot (*sic*) in the Behar Province." The first part of Hicky's announcement is pure malicious gossip, for Grand, satisfied with the results of his "eternal separation" from Catherine and with having Francis' *sicca* rupees still in his pocket, was much too engrossed in substantial material promotion to concern himself with the spiritual freedom of a divorce. The latter portion of the article, however, was correct. Grand had succeeded in getting Hastings to transfer him to the Behar Provinces as Collector of Revenues and Magistrate at Tirhoot and Hajeepore. Here, for a few years, he enjoyed the pleasure of his lands, houses, horses, and boats and lived in the comfortable security of a good office and a flourishing private fortune derived from the "manufacture of indigo after the European manner."

II

At four o'clock on an October morning, after a long, tedious, and much-delayed voyage of ten months, Philip Francis arrived at Dover. That same night at ten o'clock he entered the front door of his London house in Harley Street and was received with joyful tears and the tenderest of welcomes by his wife and children.

Though happy in the comfort of his English home, Francis could never free himself from thoughts of India. The anguish of his failure to vanquish Hastings on his own ground festered in his mind. At last, however, he had to come to the conclusion that there were other fields, beyond the political battlefield of India, in which he might yet fight the power of his old enemy. Diligently he had busied himself with these thoughts during the long voyage home. No sooner did he set foot in England than, determined as ever to have his way, he started on a vehement campaign to embitter the public mind against the Governor-General of Bengal.

The years that followed brought Francis honors, social position, a seat in the House of Commons, and a knighthood, but they brought him, too, the painful realization that everything connected with his Indian career was doomed to end against a blank wall of baffled bankruptcy. Though he did eventually succeed in getting a motion by Burke to impeach Warren Hastings before the House of Lords, the fruits of his labors were failure and disappointment. Small wonder that at the end of that historic trial, these bitter words forced themselves to his lips: "I will never be concerned in impeaching anybody. The impeachment of Mr. Hastings has cured me of that folly. *I* was tried and *he* was acquitted . . ."

On his return from India, Francis once more took up the threads of his domestic life and showed himself a kind and affectionate father and a courteous and mindful husband. He treated Mrs. Francis with his old, charmingly playful attachment and most sincerely believed that in her he did indeed possess "the best girl in the world" as a wife. But he had not forgotten Catherine—nor ever would. Neither had she forgotten him, though the months of their separation brought her a strange adventure which had curious and far-reaching influences on her life.

III

The Dutch ship which that December day carried Catherine from India, picked her way among the budgerows, snake-boats, commerical vessels, and sloops of war that lay in Diamond Harbor. Once clear of the assembled shipping she headed for the open sea with sails fanned by a light breeze.

Wrapped in a long, loose cloak Catherine leaned upon the taffrail and watched the Indian shore recede. Her thoughts were wild and jumbled like the ever-changing cadences of a symphony by a mad composer. The only harmonious theme in the symphonic confusion was her memory of Francis, his tenderness, his favors that had brought her happiness, and his voice which had always pleased her ears with soft, soothing words. All the excitement of her adventurous trip, of going to Paris, was gone. She felt terribly forlorn, utterly helpless and alone. Heartache and self-pity sent the tears pouring down her cheeks. Silently she cried, her eyes straining to catch the last faint outline of the Indian coast etched upon the distant horizon. At last, wearied beyond endurance by the agitation of her mind and her emotions, she sought the privacy of her uncomfortable cabin. . . .

The first lap of Catherine's voyage from Calcutta to the Cape passed uneventfully. Though a formidable undertaking, its dangers and difficulties were not accentuated by calms or storms, adverse currents or disease, pirates or enemy ships prowling the ocean highway. The weeks passed slowly. There were days when the sea was smooth as glass and the breeze so gentle that it carried the ship onward under easy sail. There were nights of ethereal beauty when the moon sailed the cloudless sky like a phantom vessel. With each day Catherine's boredom increased. Beset by ennui, she wished with fervor even for some untoward excitement to break the endless monotony of days and nights. She had long since tired of watching schools of dolphin gamboling or the leaping flying fish that banged blindly against the sails and dropped upon the deck.

But at last, with a stiff breeze taking the ship around the southern promontory of Africa, the end of the first lap of the voyage was in sight. One morning land loomed out of the mists and the Cape of Good Hope, like a maiden shyly revealing herself to her lover, came into view. First Lion's Head appeared, beckoning a friendly greeting to the eager watchers standing on the deck of the Dutch ship, then Table Mountain, its rocky face half hidden by a curtain of frothy white clouds. Then, looking no bigger than the Lilliputian homes of dolls, low white houses could be seen nestling in the green enbowering vegetation of the mountain slopes.

The Dutch ship remained at the Cape for several days. Fresh water was taken on board and the larders were restocked with vegetables, fruit, and meat. While she was being reprovisioned, her passengers explored the settlement which Holland had planted more than a century before at the tip of the dark continent of Africa. Catherine wandered about the town and admired the clean square houses with their ornamental pediments and architraves. She saw prosperous burghers smoking long pipes on their high *stoeps,* and groups of slaves walking through the streets carrying loads of wood on their backs. She drove out to Constantia where in the vineyards heavy bunches of grapes were purpling in the sun.

Then the time came for the Dutch ship to go on her way. Several new passengers embarked on the day of sailing, among them a young gentleman in the employment of the Madras establishment of India.

Chapter Nine

I

A voyage from the Cape to Europe in 1781 was a prodigious venture and extremely tedious. Small wonder that the young man from Madras boarded the Dutch ship in a mood of philosophic stoicism. Yet scarcely had the East Indiaman slipped out of Table Bay when his mood changed, for on deck one day he beheld the most beautiful woman he had ever seen. . . . It was Catherine Grand.

Catherine had looked forward with terror to the interminable days of ennui that lay before her on the long route to Texel. But the acquaintanceship of Thomas Lewin of the Madras Civil Service stirred her out of her sadness and depression. So gay and charming was this fellow passenger that he completely dispelled her loneliness and boredom.

A blood and dandy of his time both in temperament and accomplishments, Lewin was nevertheless neither a fop nor a fool. Exceptionally capable and possessed of a brilliant mind, at twenty-eight he had already made a name and fortune for himself in India. He had gone out to Madras as a writer, and his ability eventually secured him the office of private secretary to the Governor. Two months prior to Catherine's departure from Calcutta the President and Council of the Fort of St. George at Madras, fully assured of his courage and discretion, delegated him to carry dispatches to the Honourable Company in England "relative to the War in the Carnatic" which was then being waged against the ferocious Hyder Ali and his French allies. Since it was essential that he should lose no time in reaching his destination it was arranged that he should sail from Pondicherry on the first available ship. This happened to be His Majesty's sloop of war *Nymph*, bound for the Cape of Good Hope. From the Cape it was his intention to proceed on his mission by the first neutral vessel bound for Europe. The news that Holland had joined the maritime powers in the war against England had not yet reached the Cape on his arrival there, and he therefore reembarked on the Dutch ship in which Catherine was voyaging, believing it, in all good faith, to be a neutral vessel.

Slight and good-looking, Lewin combined the gallantry of fashionable society with true courtesy and grace. He was extremely rich and as liberal with his wealth as with his compliments. A talented musician—he performed with skill on the violin and violoncello—he was a good chess player too, a fine dancer, and a gentleman of great amiability and wit. In innumerable ways he commended himself to Catherine's goodwill. So deeply did he ingratiate himself in her favor that very soon the voyage which had begun with apprehension for both of them, developed into an interlude of happiness and delight.

Then one day as the Dutch ship plowed her way across the Atlantic with the shores of Europe close at hand, she was waylaid by two French ships of war. Willy-nilly they changed the East Indiaman's course and carried her into Cadiz Bay. Fortunately Lewin managed to destroy his dispatches in time and, through his cabin window, had the satisfaction of watching them sink beneath the deep oblivion of the ocean. Arriving at Cadiz uncompromised by diplomatic papers, he soon secured permission to proceed on his way. However, the thought of leaving Catherine behind was unbearable and he begged her to throw in her lot with him. There was no withstanding Thomas Lewin's winning ways. Catherine, weak and tenderhearted, surrendered to his entreaties and together they left Cadiz for Lisbon, where they boarded a Portuguese ship bound for London.

II

To censure Catherine for this, her second surrender to temptation, would be easy. But there were extenuating circumstances in her case. She was at this time, it is well to bear in mind, just eighteen. She was beautiful and capricious. She loved the good things of life—riches, fine clothes, enjoyment, and the spice and flavor of romantic lovemaking. Besides which, she had neither the strength of character to withstand the lack of essential creature comforts nor the temperament suited to fight the horrors of boredom. Her pleasures were primarily of the senses, yet she was neither voluptuous, carnal, nor depraved. Life for her had to be all *amourettes* and enjoyment or it was not worthwhile. Affection and admiration were as necessary to her as eating and drinking. And these joys Thomas Lewin gave her with surpassing liberality. His gallant praises fell like music on her ears.

She was not deliberately faithless to the memory of her idyllic days with Philip Francis. At first she played her coquetting game with the delightful young man from Madras rather like a child enchanted by a new toy. Then, almost before she was aware of what was happening, the amusing flirtation developed into a sentimental attachment. But though her heart was stirred by Thomas Lewin, who had transformed the terrors and tedium of the voyage into a fantasy, her affection for Philip Francis remained unchanged.

So, perhaps, the worst that can be said of Catherine is that she possessed all the frailties of womankind and that, inherently, she was amoral. The best, that she was very young and "blest with as great a beauty as Nature durst bestow."

III

Thomas and Catherine arrived in London in the summer of 1781. The Patriot King George III, who "gloried in the name of Briton," had been on the throne for twenty-one years; Lord North had been Prime Minister for eleven; the disastrous American War of Independence was drawing to its close; Burke, Fox, and Sheridan were girding their loins; society was not based so much on wealth as on ladies and gentlemen and, like the voice of the turtle, the younger Pitt was making himself heard in the land.

The young couple set up house together in Russell Place, Fitzroy Square, and entered with zest into all the gaieties and diversions which London offered in profusion. They sauntered along the fragrant, lamp-starred walks of Vauxhall Gardens, made love in the labyrinths, watched the glittering Cascade play, and saw Horace Walpole listening to the music makers in the temple. They went to Ranelagh to revel in the masquerades held in the gilded Rotunda, and to the Pantheon in the Oxford Road, hung with lamps of green and purple glass, where Dr. Johnson often wandered with Boswell at his heels. On Sunday evenings they attended fashion's latest amusement, the promenade, held in Mrs. Cornelys' magnificent suite of rooms in Soho, where the highest in the land rubbed shoulders with pretty little milliners of humblest origin.

Thomas spent his money extravagantly on entertainment and amusement. He dressed with perfect taste in satins of the latest hues, and swaggered down the Mall with the best of the *haut-ton*, a tasseled cane dangling from his wrist. He went to Rymer for his boots and to Wagner for his hats. He attired Catherine in fine hooped gowns glittering with silver lace, gave her charming gifts, fans and trinkets and jewelry, and introduced her to the dashing bloods of the town. But she did not meet women of his own class. Ladies of high society, though finding it perfectly natural for a young man of fashion to practice and understand the art of mistresses, saw to it that he kept the game within the limits of well defined rules.

For Catherine, this summer in England passed with gaiety and excitement. Then, having tasted all its pleasures, Thomas Lewin suddenly wearied of London. Paris was calling him. In September, just a month before Philip Francis arrived at Dover, he departed for the French capital, taking Catherine with him.

BOOK IV

The Years Between

Chapter One

I

Already there were men in France in 1782 who dreamed that the millennium was close at hand. Though the profoundly ignorant masses, desperately occupied with the problem of existing under the most crushing poverty, took no interest in these dreams, the intelligentsia filled itself with the teachings of Voltaire and Jean Jacques Rousseau. The king and queen, busily occupied with their own amusements, gave little thought to social problems. The virtuous, irresolute and unfortunate Louis XVI sat on the throne in the attitude of his mighty forebears. But his tongue was unattuned to the language of despotic sovereignty. He preferred the thrill of the hunting field and the art of the smithy to the intricate machinations of state affairs. Marie Antoinette, his queen, heedlessly extravagant, and with no capacity for statecraft, gave herself up wholeheartedly to the joys of the rococo kingdom she had established at the Trianon, and neglected the Court of Versailles. It was a hazardous thing to do. An idle, disregarded court is always dangerous, and dangerously now it began to beguile away its unoccupied hours. Fashionable society, however, thought of nothing but itself. Following the queen's lead, it danced in orgiastic folly on the brilliantly illuminated stage of Paris, little dreaming that the dark curtain in the background was soon to rise on the terrors of the Revolution.

There was much wit and gaiety in the Paris of 1782 among people of *ton*. Their manners were perfect on the surface and grossly obscene below it. They possessed little character. Virtue and modesty "hung by a button." Vice was considered a "gentlemanly foible," provided it was practiced in the right manner.

Men of fashion preferred not to marry. Marriage was an institution suitable only for the poor and the middle class. It was a burden to the rich. Mistresses were the mode and, though "men were eager to possess and women anxious to captivate," love, according to the dictates of prevailing fashion, had to be bought. Novelty was the all-important recommendation. Anything and everything that was new and unusual was considered exciting —new books, new dishes, new actors and actresses, a new opera, a new hairdresser, or a new amour. Extravagant nothings were uttered in the most effusive language. National events were but passing topics of conversation. The burning questions of the day were fashions, scandals, love intrigues, the rise and fall of stocks and shares, and whether the curtain at the Opéra would rise at the appointed time. Clothes were brilliant, flamboyant, and unusual. Ladies' gowns were enormous in proportion, ladies' heads so bejeweled and beribboned that they could squeeze into a carriage only with the greatest difficulty. Gentlemen swaggered down the dirty streets in silks and satins and velvets of gorgeous coloring, their hats tucked under their arms for fear of disarranging their wigs. Superciliously they quizzed the common herd about them, sniffing their contempt of it out of elaborately ornamented snuffboxes in the belief that the world had been created solely for their pleasure.

II

Onto this stage set so lavishly for levity and frivolity, Thomas Lewin led Catherine Grand, little more than a child and, despite her experience of life, far from being a woman of the world. Unhesitatingly she accepted the spirit of the times and joined the bright and lively company that danced and wined and played at love with such ardor and abandon on the very brink of the Revolution. The extravagant modes of society intoxicated her. Light, carefree, and avid for admiration, she loved enjoyment, beautiful clothes, jewels, lively company, the fragrance of fashionable coquetry, and all the good things of the world.

Life for Catherine, at the moment, held no other significance than pleasure. And because she possessed neither much intelligence nor great strength of character, ennui was her greatest terror. But Thomas Lewin saw to it that she never suffered boredom. Her beauty (which brought astonishment even into the jaded eyes of fashionable Paris), added to his money and social rank, assured her position in frivolous society. In short, it did not take long for her to become a puppet in a community of puppets. Lewin proved a kind and generous protector. He gave her all the sweetmeats of life which she so passionately desired—entertainment, amusement, gay company, beautiful clothes and jewels. He even allowed her an account at the jeweler of Monsieur at the Palais-Royal where, in the month of April, her liabilities stood at as high a figure as 4,816 livres.

III

Catherine was to prove but an incident in Thomas Lewin's gay life. He had come to Paris a dandy accustomed to associate with all the young bloods of the period, well armed with a number of introductions to aristocratic families. When his affair with Madame Grand began to lose some of its charm, he put these introductions to good use. His personality won such high favor for him among the ladies and gentlemen of the nobility that very soon he began to spend less and less time with Catherine and the young bloods of the town. Frequently in these days he joined the Royal hunt at Marly; more often still he was to be seen driving four-in-hand with his aristocratic friends. . . . The romantic interlude with Catherine was over. There were no scenes at the final parting. It was amicable and affectionate and, generous as ever, Lewin settled an annuity on the beautiful girl who for a few brief months had given him so much delight.

The break with Lewin left Catherine neither dispirited nor heartbroken. There seemed nothing extraordinary to her in what had happened. They had once meant something to each other, but now the affair had lost its meaning. A charming episode had come to an end.

Catherine's short life had been an amazing one. She had met and married George François Grand when she was not yet fifteen. To him, gladly and unquestioningly, she had given her beauty and her love. . . . At sixteen Philip Francis had brought her the first taste of despair, yet in the end boredom and vainglory drove her into his arms. His rank, his gallantry, and his love had touched her heart with passion and gratitude. . . . Then once again ennui made her embark on a sentimental interlude with Thomas Lewin, whose enchanting personality and warm generosity won her affection. . . . Love, passion, and affection—each in turn had come into her life, and in that order, so that already, at twenty, her responses might seem to be growing shallower. But this was not so. Gay, flighty, and emotional she certainly was, but she had a middle-class regard for respectability and possessed neither the enterprise nor the cold daring of an adventuress. She was indolent, impressionable, and boredom was her greatest enemy.

With the Lewin episode at an end, Catherine's mood changed. Her deep-rooted desire for bourgeois respectability triumphed over her passion for the frivolities of the gay society into which Thomas had initiated her; this resulted in her seeking out the companionship of a worthy widowed lady, a relative on her father's side. She had been in regular correspondence with Francis ever since his return to England. Apparently he had learned nothing of the romantic little play which began on the Dutch ship bound for Texel and ended so soon afterward in Paris. He wrote to a friend in India at this time that his lovely lady was "creditably established in Paris in the society of Madame Vanlée."

A further proof of Catherine's determination to follow the paths of propriety is the fact that, having written to Francis of a proposed holiday at Spa and receiving an answer from him that he would join her there, she replied immediately and firmly that though she "acknowledged her affection for him and for no one else," she would not on any account renew "the improper part of her intercourse with him." Francis, however, "for the pleasure of seeing her again," made the journey and, since he traveled from England on several later occasions with the express purpose of visiting her in Paris and in Spa, her charms obviously still possessed their attraction for him. Many years afterward he praised her in no uncertain manner to the second Mrs. Francis when he declared in all sincerity that "her understanding was much better than the world allowed; her education had been neglected, but her firmness in returning to the paths of propriety, which was so difficult in her situation, pursued by the man she loved, was a convincing proof of it."

After her friendly reunion with Francis at Spa and when she was twenty-one years of age, Catherine had her portrait painted by one of the most fashionable artists of the day, the talented Madame Vigée-Lebrun. As her husband used almost the whole of the richly furnished apartment in the Rue de Cléry as a picture gallery, Madame Lebrun had to content herself with two very simply furnished rooms in which she painted and received the assemblies which gathered there each day. The rooms were always crowded, even when Madame was busy with palette and brush. It was a fashionable, gallant, and witty company of ladies and gentlemen that Catherine met while she sat posing for her portrait. In and out of the rooms strolled the elegant visitors, lorgnettes gracefully lifted to appraise first the sitter then the likeness on the artist's easel. If the ladies were sometimes ambiguous in their commendation, the gentlemen assuredly took no pains to hide their preferences.

Madame Lebrun depicted her charming sitter in an attitude of graceful repose, seated in a deep armchair, her right arm resting on a green velvet cushion, an open letter in her hand. To this day this portrait remains the most enchanting likeness of the "beautiful Indian." She seems lost in thought. Dreams lie in her large, soft blue eyes. Her dress, in which blue, white, and gray blend and mingle to form a shimmering texture, is of refined severity. A fichu of white muslin, daintily secured on the bosom by a flowing bow of blue ribbon, is its only ornament. Her golden hair falls in curls on her bare neck and is raised high off the forehead to form an aureole of light in which nestles another broad blue bow. Her chin, round and finely chiseled, is slightly raised; her small nose is delicately tilted; her lips are parted in a smile that matches the soft languor of her eyes.

All Paris acclaimed it a magnificent portrait. The artist had in truth caught the mood and spirit of Catherine Grand, her indolence and freshness, her gentleness and amiability. Yet there were many who said that, vivid as the likeness was, so rare a beauty as that of Madame Grand could never be quite captured on canvas with paint and brush, even by so consummate an artist as Madame Lebrun.

Chapter Two

I

Paris was agog with excitement. Already at an early hour of the morning the streets were choked with vehicles and pedestrians hurrying onward, ever onward, in the direction of the Tuileries Gardens. From behind the slightly drawn velvet curtains of their equipages courtesans flashed tantalizing glances at gentlemen on horseback; the haughty eyes of great ladies looked with disdain at working men and women, dressed in their best clothes, hurrying out of the way of shining carriage wheels. And Catherine Grand, pale and trembling with excitement, sat in a cab beside Madame Vanlée. It was December 1, 1783, that memorable day on which, from the Gardens of the Tuileries, Monsieur Robert and an intrepid companion were to rise up into the air in a balloon for the first time.

As early as dawn the Gardens had begun to fill with a vast and varied crowd of expectant and awed watchers. As the winter sun climbed the sky, the crowd increased till the very gates were forced and the railings torn down. When the moment for the strange and fearful ascent arrived and the daring physicists climbed into their curious machine, a hush fell on the vast conclave. Dear God, what would be the end of this great adventure with Nature and the elements! The aeronauts faced the crowd. To France, nay to the whole world, they were about to prove that "inflammatory air, or as the knowing ones call it, gaz," was lighter than the atmosphere, and "if enclosed in a very light machine must rise of itself."

Seconds slipped by. Slowly the balloon rose in the air. Transfixed with emotion the crowd watched in poignant silence. The envelope of gas began to soar higher and still higher into the sky. Trembling women, swayed by fear and pity for the brave aeronauts, burst into loud weeping and fell upon their knees to pray; men, dumb with awe, stood wide-eyed, hands uplifted in astonishment and admiration. Majestically the balloon sailed above the heads of the crowd. Then, suddenly, as if assured of victory, the aeronauts dipped their flags in salute. In reply a thundering cheer that seemed to make the sky vibrate rose from the two hundred thousand spectators, moved by a strange and fearful emotion in the Gardens of the Tuileries.

Hours later the crowd dispersed. Enraptured, Catherine Grand returned to her home with Madame Vanlée. Tears ran down her cheeks, and she was filled with joy and awed admiration for the two daring physicists who had that day so nobly conquered air and space. . . .

Four months later she witnessed another historical event, the first public performance of Beaumarchais' *The Marriage of Figaro,* a satirical play on matters political and social, which for three years had been banned by the king and the censors because it reviled and inveighed too dangerously against prisons of state and *lettres de cachet.* The prohibition of the play aroused great public curiosity, a curiosity which, fermenting day by day, gave rise to such heated excitement that serious disturbances were prevented only by the promise that the play would be produced eventually. But the king's consent had to be wrested from him by deception. Tactfully it was hinted to him that since the play would unquestionably prove a failure, he could magnanimously soothe the public's inquisitiveness through disappointment and thus gain a moral victory. The ban was removed. Immediately a brilliant cast, which included the celebrated actor Dazincourt as Figaro, and Mesdemoiselles Contat and Sainval in the roles of Suzanne and the Countess of Almaviva, was assembled and rehearsals began.

So great a crowd assembled for the opening night at the Français that no carriage could get near the theater. Just before the curtain went up the mob drove away the guard in a rush, and forced the theater door open. By this time Catherine was comfortably installed in her curtained box with her cushions and her candles, her pet dog and her footwarmer, and a charming little fan with a tiny mirror in its handle through which, unseen, she was able to observe all that went on. And Philip Francis was at her side. Once more he had journeyed to Paris for the sole pleasure of seeing her.

In a *loge grillée* sat the author Monsieur Beaumarchais with the Abbé de Calonne and the Abbé Sabatier de Castres, critic and littérateur, to keep him company; in another the Comte d'Artois waited with burning impatience for the first glimpse of Mademoiselle Contat. Behind the thick silk curtains of the boxes were seen magnificently gowned ladies with flashing jewels and astonishingly original hairdress. The vivacious Countess de Polignac, friend of the queen, dined in her box that night; so did the fascinating and talented Madame de Genlis and the lackadaisical Princesse de Lamballe. The queen herself arrived only when the play was about to begin.

Loud applause greeted the fall of the last curtain. Beaumarchais had triumphed. The play was an overwhelming success. With a shrug Versailles accepted its defeat. But the play set Paris talking, now loudly, now in soft conspiratorial whispers, for *The Marriage of Figaro* had given men whose minds were already saturated with the teachings of the Philosophers much food for thought.

II

For a time, Catherine painstakingly resisted the seductive influence of gay Parisian society and kept rigidly to the path of propriety. Refusing monetary help from Francis, she continued to live in the company of Madame Vanlée on the annuity which Thomas Lewin had settled on her.

But gradually, very gradually and slowly, like a cat stealthily pursuing a mouse, her old enemy ennui began to stalk her waking hours. She began to yearn for the gaiety and luxuries to which both Francis and Lewin had accustomed her. Under Madame Vanlée's roof even respectability grew irksome. At last, defeated by boredom, she decided to set up an establishment of her own. She rented a house from a Monsieur de Presle. It was situated in the Rue Sentier. Valdec Delessart, a banker of great wealth, who was to become a minister of the Legislative within a few years, was her next door neighbor.

But Catherine soon found herself deeply involved in money matters. Her annuity, though generous and sufficient to provide for a comfortable home, left her little in hand for the luxuries that she so passionately desired. She longed to live the life of a woman of fashion with money enough to engage the services of a good dressmaker and to enable her to acquire fine jewels, fans, shoe buckles, ribbons, and laces. In addition, she wished for a carriage and horses, for how else could a woman of fashion, in the course of one short day, manage to pay calls, shop, drive in the Bois, and later put in an appearance at a ball, the theater, or the Opéra? With such desires pressing for fulfilment, one career only lay open before her, a career in which her beauty, her childlike naïveté, and her extraordinary practical common sense, assured her unlimited success. Unresistingly and, indeed, deliberately, she allowed the tide of her desires to carry her into the harbor of courtesanship. Valdec Delessart, her next door neighbor, who had fallen passionately in love with her, became her first lover. . . .

For more than two years Delessart was to be "the superintendent of the finances" of her house. Generously he made up the deficit between her annuity and the money she spent on the upkeep of a splendid establishment. She applied to him for everything. He paid even such meager trifles as the wages of a maid and a few francs for the repair of a watch. In 1786 she had her house completely renovated with new wallpaper, tapestries, and gilding. Her boudoir was made particularly enchanting with "four large panels with arabesques of an English green background, and pink cameos and painted pilasters framing the panels." To the painters alone, on this occasion, Delessart paid the sum of 1,370 livres.

Catherine now began to entertain on a lavish scale. Since she could command as much money as she needed, she lived in great style. She dressed tastefully and beautifully, patronized the best milliners and dressmakers, and bought only the finest jewels, ribbons, and feathers. . . . The "beautiful Indian" soon became the most glamorous courtesan in that gay, extravagant, reckless society that danced so heedlessly beneath the lowering clouds of the approaching deluge.

On February 22, 1787, she gave a great ball at her house in the Rue Sentier which set all Paris talking. Venus had never looked more beautiful than Catherine did that night in "a tight-fitting tunic of white taffeta trimmed with pink fringe; a skirt of white crêpe striped with white satin ribbon, spangled with silver and bordered with the same ribbon, the hem bordered similarly with laurel flowers; under-sleeves of white crêpe with spangles, tied up with a bracelet of pink larkspur, and a ruche of tulle round the bodice." This magnificent costume cost 264 livres. Delessart paid for the dress as well as the sum of 288 livres for the violins. He looked very handsome that night, though with contrasting modesty he had paid but nine livres for "a sword-knot of violet ribbon with marigold spots" which adorned his suit for the occasion.

Balls and the company of gay society did not, however, occupy all Catherine's time. She still clung desperately to the ruins of respectability. And strange as it may seem, her beauty and air of refinement opened the door of many a fine mansion which, as a rule, was sternly sealed against women of her profession. Even the dignified Madame Delessart, her lover's mother, received her regularly and willingly. It was here in Madame Delessart's house that she made the acquaintance of the young Baron de Frénilly to whom at first she paid little attention, since at the time she considered him a mere child. Frénilly was enchanted by her loveliness from the moment he first set eyes upon her. In his memoirs, years later, he etched a word picture of Catherine at this time, "in the radiance of youth, with incomparable teeth, a transparent whiteness and a mass of fair hair such as was to be seen nowhere." To this he added with the sagacity of age: "She was a good woman at bottom—*la belle et la bête* at one and the same time!"

In addition to setting herself assiduously to acquire a certain measure of respectability, Catherine now began to pay a considerable amount of attention to the improvement of her mind. She read a great deal, received such newspapers as the *Affiches de Paris* and *Le Journal Général de France* regularly, subscribed to the *Lycée des Arts de Laharpe*, and paid 576 livres for Buffon's *Natural History* in thirty-two volumes, edited by Didot. And in the evening she invariably attended the Opéra, the Théâtre des Italiens, or the Comédie Française, having a private box in each place.

For two years Delessart kept his "position" in her affections and in the management of her financial affairs. At the end of that time his place was taken by a delightful young gentleman from the Faubourg Saint-Honoré, a district as sacred to bankers and men of finance as the environs of the Faubourg Saint-Germain were to the nobility. This young man was a wealthy "legal representative of an agent of Exchange"—in short, a stockbroker's attorney—and he proved as charming and gallant as his name, which was Rilliet-Plantamour.

It was now the year 1787. The air had grown thick and heavy with a cold, ominous, restrained silence. The horrid affair of the Diamond Necklace had caused the anger against Marie Antoinette to rise to a virulent pitch. No longer were the familiar cries of *Vive la Reine* heard in the streets of Paris. Dissatisfaction was spreading like an ugly sore. The masses, irritable and excited, were no longer vague in their desire for a new order. In their ears rang the strange tales that were being told by the volunteers who had recently returned from fighting in the American War of Independence, tales of a country of liberty and fraternity where there were no king or queen or nobles, but only free and equal citizens. . . . France seethed with unrest. In Paris itself the teachings of Voltaire and Jean Jacques Rousseau were rapidly fermenting. . . . And in the background the Bastille stood frowning and fierce, threatening unfathomable menace.

Her head a little on one side, she looked at him intently. A gentle, almost motherly smile lay on her mouth. Then she moved, so that the curtain folds hid her as if in an alcove. "Come here, *mon ami*," she said softly, holding out her hands. Eagerly he caught them and covered them with kisses. "There now," she soothed him. "There now." And then: "How old are you, *mon cher*?" she asked.

"I am eighteen, madame."

"Eighteen? And I am twenty-six."

"What does that matter?" he cried passionately.

"Matter? Monsieur, I am much too old for you. I do not wish to be your mistress. Do not let me have to say that again. I shall have to send you away forever, my child, if you do not stop worrying me. . . . But we could be friends."

"I cannot be only your friend," he cried hotly.

"No?" Slowly she turned from him and sat down among her cushions. "Very well then, since we cannot be friends I must send you away . . ."

He stood silent as a ghost among the shadows, and she sat watching the stage. After some minutes she spoke again. "Take up the glasses, *mon ami*," she said gently, "and tell me who is here tonight."

For a moment he hesitated before obeying her soft command. Carefully he scanned the stalls and boxes and repeated the names of people in the audience. She barely listened to what he was saying. His voice went on and on. "Madame de Polignac, the Vicomte de Lambertye, Madame Lebrun, Monsieur Edouard Dillon—"

She leaned sharply forward. "Monsieur Dillon, did you say?" she asked.

"Yes, madame, in the second box on the right."

A smile touched her lips. While the young nobleman's voice droned on she played with her fan so that the little mirror in the handle caught and held the reflection of the man in the second box on the right. At last she closed her fan but sat gazing at him so fixedly that her eyes attracted his. He looked at her, looked away, then looked again. A few minutes later he left his box.

Catherine had long been fascinated by Edouard Dillon, but, deeply occupied with a passionate liaison, he had paid her little attention. Small wonder then that when he entered her box that evening she felt like a general who had won a great victory.

"Am I an intruder?" he asked as he bent down to kiss her fingertips.

"Not in the least, monsieur."

He sat down in a chair immediately behind her, half hidden by the curtains. It was the chair in which the young nobleman, all through the first act, had sat babbling of his love. But now he had moved to the back of the box and stood there in the shadows, hot tears burning his eyes. Catherine had completely forgotten his existence. At last, blind with anger and jealousy, he fled from the box. She did not even notice that he had gone. Edouard Dillon was close beside her, gallant and romantic, so very much the fashion among the greatest ladies in Paris.

II

Edouard Dillon possessed a profound knowledge of the world, boundless self-assurance, perfect manners, and exquisite wit. His astonishing good looks had earned for him the nickname of "Handsome." Women found him as fascinating as *le diable* himself. He moved in the highest circles. At one time he was alleged to be Madame de Polignac's lover; at another the intimate of the Queen. Certainly he was frequently out hunting with the royal party, and often at the Trianon to rehearse the figures of a quadrille with Marie Antoinette. Such visits were enough for a jealous court to spread fresh scandals about the hated Austrian woman.

Stories about daredevil Dillon were always being bandied about in society. Catherine knew all of them. How she had laughed at his encounter with the provincial gentleman! The whole thing had begun so absurdly, at a supper party given at the house of one of the king's ministers. Dillon, deeply engrossed in a lady who, for the moment, possessed his tenderest affections, found himself rudely interrupted by a doltish gentleman from the provinces who sat facing him across the table.

"Monsieur Dillon," said the man, fingering some small jars which stood before him, "I should like to ask you what these pots are for."

"*À l'avoine*," answered Dillon curtly.

The provincial gentleman flushed red as a beetroot. Unaware that "*pots à l'avoine*" were a dish very much in fashion at the moment, he took the word at its literal meaning which signified "for oats." *Mon Dieu*, did that Parisian fop take him for a horse! Never before had he been so deeply insulted. "Indeed, monsieur," he answered sharply. "Then I shall send you some straw!"

Edouard made no reply. Calmly he continued his conversation with the lovely lady at his side. But immediately after supper when the ladies had withdrawn, he delivered his challenge, the only possible reply a gentleman could give to so offensive a retort. The meeting was arranged for the following day. Edouard chose an hour just before noon, for he strongly objected to being disturbed too early in the morning. When the provincial gentleman arrived at his opponent's house next day at the appointed time, Edouard was not quite ready to receive him. He had not yet finished dressing. He apologized charmingly for the delay, and, not one whit perturbed, continued his toilet in the most leisurely manner.

"Sir, if you have no business calling you elsewhere," he said a moment later, putting the finishing touches to his cravat, "may I suggest that we go to the wood of Vincennes? You see, I am dining at Saint Maur afterward and I see that I shall barely have time to keep my appointment."

The provincial gentleman's eyes bulged in their sockets.

"Then you intend—!" he exclaimed aghast.

"Certainly, sir," Dillon interrupted him calmly. "I intend to dine at Saint Maur after I have killed you, for I gave my promise last night to Madame de—"

The duel was fought in the wood of Vincennes. But Dillon kept only one of his promises. He dined at Saint Maur.

III

Dillon had arrived at the Opera alone and in a mood of black dejection. On the following day he was leaving Paris. All the plans for his departure were complete. It was not business but the sudden rupture of a passionate liaison which had made him decide to forsake for a while the city and the pleasures that he loved. In a voyage to the East he hoped to find forgetfulness of the injuries his heart and his vanity had suffered.

As he sat in his box, his eyes fixed unseeingly on the stage, he was thinking: "Tomorrow I shall be gone. When shall I again sit here in this great building with the voices of singers echoing in my ears? The East! I am going to the distant and savage East. I am leaving Paris. This is my last night of civilization. My last night. Perhaps the sight of the beautiful shoulders of Parisian women gleaming soft and white under the yellow candlelight will be lost to me forever. . . ." Suddenly he became aware of someone staring at him with fixed concentration. He turned his head sharply in that direction and saw Madame Grand watching him from her box. Indolently he raised his spyglass and fixed it on her. *Mon Dieu,* she was indeed incredibly beautiful! Was it true, he wondered, that she understood the most subtle nuances of love better than any other woman in Paris, as he had heard positively asserted? Then why had he neglected her? He should have made it his business to know her better. Now, alas, it was too late. He was leaving Paris.

He continued to watch Catherine, and second by second his mood changed. An all-devouring curiosity consumed him. He said to himself: "I am leaving for the perilous East. This is my last night in Paris. No man has a right to spend his last night alone. . . ." The next instant he left his box.

IV

Before the curtain came down on the second act Catherine left the Opera. Following her along the wide corridor, the rustle of her skirts sounded to Edouard Dillon like the sound of the sea as it rushes past the bows of a ship. When they reached the front door she ordered her carriage. A minute later, with Dillon beside her, the carriage moved off, the hoofs of the two superb bays clattering out a metallic obbligato on the cobblestones. There were few vehicles and pedestrians in the streets, but ever and again a linkman, swinging his lantern, sauntered into view calling his monstrously raucous cry, "Here's a light, here's a light," loudly into the night.

In the dark interior of the carriage Catherine sat erect and stately as a princess, smiling to herself. Edouard Dillon, friend of Madame de Polignac and of the queen, for whom she had long had a secret passion, was at last riding in her carriage! The most sought-after man in the fashionable world of Paris had, of his own free will, chosen to spend his last night in France not with his august friends in the mighty circles of the Trianon, but in supping alone with her, Catherine Grand. Her heart was afire with triumph.

When the carriage stopped before her house in the Rue Sentier, she led Dillon into a room lit with many candles. The table was decorated with flowers and set for two. She took off her velvet cloak and laid it on a chair. A maid appeared. "Is everything ready?" she asked.

"Yes, madame."

"Good. Come, monsieur." She made him sit down at the table, facing her. The maid brought in the supper.

"If there is a ring at the door," she told the maid who was about to withdraw, "say I am in bed and asleep and must not be disturbed on any account. Do you understand? Not on any account."

"Yes, madame." Quietly the maid shut the door.

The food was delicious, the wine excellent. The minutes sped by on gossamer wings. Edouard was charming. He felt extremely happy. Watching her across the table everything about her enchanted him, her voice, her face, her supple figure, her beautiful complexion, her small tapering hands, her hair. Ah, her hair. He said: "When I am far away in distant barbaric lands, and have almost become a savage, I shall recall Paris to mind only because I shall remember your hair, madame."

"Monsieur, you tease me with too much flattery."

"Flattery, madame! Beauty cannot be flattered. It can only be adored."

She smiled at him. Her blue eyes looked at him with the innocence of a child. "You are very generous, monsieur," she said. "But, indeed, you have no conception yet of what it is really like. Shall I show you?"

"Madame, does a man dying in the desert of thirst feel satisfied with one small sip of water?"

She rose from the table. "You will pardon me for a moment, monsieur?"

He bowed, and she passed into her boudoir and closed the door. Leisurely he turned to inspect the room. It was tastefully furnished with touches of daintiness that indicated the nature of the owner. He went up to the mantelpiece and stood watching the tiny figures of a white marble clock, shaped like a temple, as they moved round and round the dome. He wondered why Catherine loved little clocks. The room was full of them.

"Shall we finish supper, monsieur?"

He turned sharply at the sound of her voice to find her standing beside the table, one hand resting on the back of the chair. She had loosened her hair and it fell in a golden cascade on her shoulders. Teasing tendrils caressed her forehead, "smooth as alabaster and white as a lily." Like a "second Eve before the Fall" she stood there "naked and unashamed." Awed, he gazed at her in silence. She smiled at him and sat down at the table.

"Do you like my hair like this, monsieur?" she asked, her eyes innocently inspecting a sugared plum that she held between her fingers.

In one stride he was at her side. He stooped and kissed her hand, then, raising a curl, pressed it to his lips. "I am enraptured, madame," he cried. "Never have I seen anything so exquisitely beautiful in all my life."

"As my hair, monsieur?"

"As your hair, madame," he answered with a bow.

She motioned him to his chair. So they finished their supper. . . .

First one little clock struck the hour of dawn and then others answered it, one by one. They were all just seconds behind each other.

He took her face between his hands and kissed her mouth, first one corner, then the other, then full on the lips. Then, gravely, he stood looking down into her eyes. They resembled violets, he thought, blue violets. His fingers caressed her loosened hair. "I am grateful, Catherine. Most deeply grateful," he said gently. "I shall ever hope that I may see you soon again."

"And I, monsieur," she answered him, "I also shall hope." Her eyes were large and blue and moist. Her hair tumbled about her shoulders like a golden waterfall. She was a courtesan. She had had many lovers. But in this moment, trembling in his arms, she seemed to him a maiden who had given him her first love.

At last he went away. The city was still asleep. He felt suddenly sad as he walked through the empty streets. . . . It was true, quite true, all that men said of Madame Grand. Better than any other woman in Paris she understood the most subtle nuances of love. He wondered vaguely what scent she used. It was delicious. *Mon Dieu,* if only he were not leaving so soon for the dangerous and distant East! But perhaps, when he returned . . . He would not stay away too long. One could not stay away too long from Paris. . . .

But Edouard Dillon was reckoning without the Furies. They kept him out of Paris for twenty-six years, and many things changed in that time—even Catherine Grand.

Chapter Four

I

Throughout France, during the terrible winter of 1787–8, death stalked hand in hand with famine, and discontent was rife. Like scarlet fever, uneasiness spread from the bourgeoisie to the common people, to whom the teachings of the Philosophers were no longer juggled words but facts. The outcry against oppression, injustice and extortionate taxation grew louder and louder. The masses had at last become articulate about the iniquities and wrongs under which they suffered. Their hearts were filled with bitter anger against the nobles and the monarchy—against the queen in particular. At the Trianon where the air was sweet with the music of Gluck and Piccinni, Marie Antoinette tried to put a restraining hand on the bridle of her vanity and extravagance. People of fashion, considering philanthropy and simplicity quite the mode, chattered artlessly of nature and philosophy and the rights of man.

But the new year which had been born in travail continued its noisy outcry, and in the Rue de Paradis, at the house of Theresia Cabarrus, wife of the Marquis de Fontenay, Mirabeau and Robespierre and Camille Desmoulins roamed among the guests, casting the first warning shadows of the approaching Revolution. The barque of state was sailing perilously across the turbulent sea of unrest. Poor, well-intentioned Louis XVI hastily summoned Necker once again to take the helm. But the ship continued to toss drunkenly. Then, in obedience to the clamor of the nobles, Louis called the States-General, that mighty assembly of Nobles, Clergy, and Commons which had not been convoked for one hundred and seventy-five years.

On May 5, 1789, the members of the States-General, some

116

in violet robes and snow-white plumes, some in dark citizenlike attire, marched in solemn procession through the streets of Versailles. Limping with the clergy came a certain Charles Maurice de Talleyrand, newly created Bishop of Autun. Versailles wore an air of gaiety and joyful celebration. Flags waved in the breeze, garlands and tapestries hung from the house fronts. The Court showed all its splendors. Never did the queen look so beautiful as she did that day in a violet, white, and silver robe, with ostrich plumes on her head. But behind her proud mask of majesty she hid a heart tortured with anguish for her dying eldest son. . . . Half Paris had come to Versailles. Yet, among all that mighty throng not one soothsayer stepped forth to announce: "Messieurs and mesdames, the curtain is up. This is the first scene of the Revolution."

For six long weeks discussions raged in the States-General, and all that time the Commons faced the drawn daggers of the nobility and the clergy. Then came the final break. Finding themselves excluded from the Hall of the Assembly by the king, the Third Estate, having declared itself the National Assembly, adjourned to a neighboring tennis court and there the members took a solemn oath not to separate until they had given France a new and better Constitution. "Tell your master," cried Mirabeau to the grand master of the ceremonies, "that we are here by the power of the people, and we shall not go hence save at the bayonet's point."

When Monsieur de Talleyrand, Bishop of Autun, threw in his lot with Mirabeau, and the lower clergy joined the National Assembly, royalty felt its authority crumbling like soft, fresh bread. Louis was in a quandary. Yet even then, if he had but taken a strong hand and declared for the Commons, the history of France might have been different. Instead, weak and vacillating, he turned for advice to the queen and his courtiers. Their counsel—an open challenge to the nation—he followed to the letter. Troops were massed on Paris and on July 11th, Necker, his only minister who was popular with the people, was dismissed and ordered to leave the kingdom without delay.

II

Since Catherine was a woman of fashion she followed its dictates slavishly. When everyone talked of nature and philosophy and virtue, she artlessly chattered of these things too. When people of *ton* took up the cry of simplicity, she joined her voice in the general clamor. And since it had become a fashionable craze to affect a wild admiration for Henry IV, former monarch of France—enthusiastically regarded by the masses as the patron saint of Paris because, it was believed, he would have liked to see a fowl in every old woman's stewpot—she too developed a passionate adoration for this long-dead king.

When philanthropy was the rage and simplicity the mode, and when it was no longer considered elegant to attire oneself in silks and satins and great panniered skirts, she took to wearing simple robes à la Jean Jacques Rousseau in lawn and batiste and woollen crepe. In the daytime she tied her coiffure with a plain ribbon; in the evening she adorned her hair with flowers in dainty garlands. Because virtue had become fashionable, she demurely covered her neck and throat with billowy fichus secured with a charming but essentially rustic brooch. She no longer wore heeled shoes and discarded her high-piled headdress with her bonnets.

Happily she gave herself up to the craze of "the villager and virginal" in fashion, modes which served to enhance her beauty. And all through the dying years of the French monarchy, whether she dressed to resemble "a divinely spiritual figure of Greuze" or a chaste village maiden, she still remained, in the eyes of the gallants of Paris, as desirable as ever.

III

The summer morning of July 12th dawned warm and bright. It was Sunday. No one yet believed that the king could have summarily dismissed Necker.

Around Paris regiments of Germans, Irish, Flemish, and Swiss lay encamped. There had been rioting in the city and though it had ceased, the atmosphere remained strangely disturbed. Streams of people were hastening to the chief revolutionary center at the Palais-Royal, but there were still peaceful men who quietly prepared to spend the day in the open with their families and friends in the Bois de Boulogne or at St. Cloud. Here and there in the streets citizens hailed each other with a wave of the hand and the cry of *Vive la liberté!*

Throughout that warm sunny morning the crowd at the Palais-Royal became greater and more excited as it waited impatiently for confirmation of the rumor that Necker had been removed from office. Only at four o'clock in the afternoon did a messenger come from Versailles. He was pale and disheveled and soaked with sweat as he told them the news. The king had spurned his people. . . . Still and silent the crowd stood, as if stricken with a strange paralysis. At this moment a shabby young man entered the Café de Foy, the very heart of the turbulent Palais-Royal. He carried a pistol in one hand. In the other he held a paper confirming the news of Necker's dismissal. It was Camille Desmoulins. He jumped on a high bench and began to speak— quickly, loudly, eloquently. He forgot his stammer. His tongue became a lash of scorpions with which he scourged the paralyzed mob into electric vehemence. He built a pyramid of angry, burning words from the topmost peak of which, suddenly, leaped the raging flame of a single call: *Aux armes, aux armes, aux armes!*

The cry was taken up by a thousand throats and then a thousand more. Moment by moment it grew in force and volume till it swept through the Palais-Royal like a devastating cyclone. To arms! To arms! roared the mob as it rushed into the streets. There it divided into two. One half swept onward to wrest weapons from the Hôtel de Ville; the other hastened to the atelier of a famous sculptor to clamor for a bust of the dismissed minister. In a flash the cause of Necker had become the cause of the nation. . . . The curtain had risen on the second scene of the Revolution.

Hour by hour the leaping flames of insurrection roared louder and louder through the streets. A new day dawned and still the conflagration spread. From church steeples the tocsin sounded its cry of alarm and the roll of drums called the people to assemble in public places. Out of the dank fever holes and dark stench-poisoned passages of the underworld poured tortured dregs of humanity, noisily demanding food. Shrill above the siren cry for arms echoed the clamorous screams: "Flour and bread! Bread and flour!" . . . The sun set; "none but children slept that night," and the terrible Bastille frowned threateningly down upon the squalor and terror and gloom of vice-ridden alleys and narrow, fetid, twisted streets.

On the morning of July 14th the mob was still without arms. But now a rumor spread that weapons were to be had in the arsenal at the Invalides and, despite the troops camped on the Champ de Mars, the Invalides was stormed. A mighty pillage began. Sabers, pikes, swords—every sort of weapon—was snatched up greedily. Then for the first time came the deafening cry: *À la Bastille!*

Menacingly the grim fortress of feudalism frowned down upon the approaching mob. The drawbridges were up. There was to be no firing unless the people attacked. . . . Later, however, one drawbridge was lowered and a body of men was allowed into the courtyard. Suddenly a volley of musketry from the fort mowed them down. . . . The smell of death rose heavily in the air. Revenge! Revenge! roared the ever-increasing mob. The heavens grew gray above the heads of the multitude shouting in unearthly fury: *La Bastille! Nous voulons la Bastille!* Smoke and flames began to rise from the cartloads of straw and hay that the besiegers set alight beside the stern walls of the impregnable fortress. Three times a deputation from the Hôtel de Ville, waving a white flag, came to offer a truce. Three times it was turned away. The mob wanted no truce. It wanted the Bastille.

The hours slipped by. Soldiers in the city defied their officers. They had seized two cannon from the arsenal of the Invalides and were bringing them up to help the besiegers. The garrison in the fortress began to show its sympathy for the mob. Only the twenty Swiss Guards still obeyed the Governor who, after a futile attempt to blow up his stronghold, agreed to surrender. The white flag was hoisted and above the shouts of "We want the Bastille" came the clarion cry: "You shall have the Bastille."

"The Governor and garrison shall march out with honors of war," ran the note of surrender.

"Let down the drawbridges," replied the mob, "and no harm shall come to you. No lives are to be taken. There will be no bloodshed. Only let down the drawbridges."

An officer of the Queen's Regiment accepted the conditions "on the word of an officer." The bridges were let down, the gates opened. In rushed the mob, a wild, demented horde. "Victory! Victory! Liberty! No quarter! No quarter!" it cried. Mad eyes bulged from their sockets and froth foamed on evil lips. Swords, pikes, clubs, and sabers flashed and splintered and in steaming streams flowed the blood of dead and dying men. Murder and infamy, hideous, cruel, and insane, added agony to agony and piled horror upon horror. Only death was merciful.

That night, while the king lay sleeping in his great palace at Versailles, the Duc de Liancourt, Grand Master of the Wardrobe, came to tell him that the Bastille had been attacked and taken by the mob.

"It is a revolt then?" he asked drowsily, raising himself on an elbow.

"Sire, it is a Revolution," answered De Liancourt.

And Louis lay down again and resumed his interrupted sleep.

IV

With the capture of the Bastille the old regime collapsed. On August 27th the Declaration of the Rights of Man was published and Mirabeau, who desired to see in France a constitutional monarchy of the English type, was the man of the moment. He had pledged himself to the king, he and his friend Talleyrand, Bishop

of Autun. They tried to work both for the king and the revolution. But even the greatest statesman cannot serve two masters, and gradually conditions in France went from bad to worse.
The gale of Revolution blew across the rising sea of turbulent
passions, whipping up a cyclonic tide that carried Danton and
Robespierre on its foaming crest. . . .

Step by step Catherine Grand wisely followed the path of the
Revolution. She made an orgy of simplicity and a minor creed
of philanthropy. When the Declaration of the Rights of Man
authoritatively decreed that, in future, class distinction must be
based only on enlightened learning and merit, she turned her attention wholeheartedly to her educational shortcomings. Assiduously she began to cultivate the powers of her mind with the
full determination not to be left stranded in the rear ranks of
this new social order. With her usual naïveté mixed with a
common-sense practicality, she started the long climb up the
ladder of knowledge and instruction by hiring a writing master
for twelve livres a month to teach her to form words with their
proper letters. Up to this time she had still been misspelling certain words with almost daring impudence. Now, too, she circum-
spectly deserted the Opéra for the Théâtre of Monsieur and the
Français and religiously read the *Journal de Paris* which Roederer
edited.

On May 1, 1790, she hired a house in the Rue d'Artois from
Monsieur Barré, an architect. Asked for a guarantor for the annual rent of this establishment which amounted to 4,200 livres,
she gave the name of a certain banker, Deputy for India at the
Assemblé Constituant. With a flourish he signed his name as
security, for, since the fall of the gallant Rilliet-Plantamour, it
was he, Louis Monneron, who had become the protector of the
loveliest courtesan in Paris and the guardian of her home and
hearth.

The house in the Rue d'Artois was a fine building, newly constructed under a slate roof, with an imposing frontage on the
street and a large courtyard. When she moved in, Catherine had

it entirely repainted and regilded. She bought new furniture and attired her servants in new livery. But everything, of course, bore the hallmark of simplicity. The house was large. It had two halls, a winding staircase, and many rooms, also a garret, stables, and a coach house. Since the beginning of the Revolution, however, she no longer used her carriage. She kept it securely locked in her coach house and, abandoning herself to the craze for simplicity, went out on foot. She wore out forty-six pairs of shoes in a single year.

One day the young Baron Frénilly came to her house in the Rue d'Artois. He had heard that she possessed a fine carriage but no horses. Ah, *mon Dieu,* but it was unbelievable that she should be deprived of so indispensable a necessity as a coach and horses! The Revolution? But still, it was inconceivable that Madame Grand's pretty feet should so much as touch the dirty cobblestones of Paris streets, even if there was a Revolution! . . . Now strange to relate, declared young Baron Frénilly, he had a fine pair of white horses. They would look perfect drawing Madame's carriage. Perfect. . . . So he talked charmingly to Catherine. His conversation made her forget for a while all about Danton and Robespierre and Mirabeau and the Declaration of the Rights of Man. He was no longer the silly boy of no consequence who had once lived in the house opposite to Valdec Delessart's mother. He had quite grown up. . . . Indeed, indeed, his white horses would look magnificent attached to her derelict carriage! . . . So one day they hitched his horses to her carriage and away they went, through the gates of Paris. . . . At young Frénilly's lakeside cottage they tried to forget the Revolution, for a few brief days, in an interlude of spring sweetness, laughter, and love.

Chapter Five

I

"When I am gone they will know what the value of me was. The miseries I have held back will burst from all sides on France. I carry in my heart the death-dirge of the French monarchy." So ran the prophecy of that shrewd statesman of great insight, that amazing genius with his high wrinkled forehead, formidable shock of hair, and deep-set eyes wild with profligacy and debauch—Mirabeau, whom some called the instrument of God. . . .

One April night he slept with two opera singers. The next day he was dead. The last man who could have interceded between the king and the people had gone to his grave a victim of debauchery. His death left Louis XVI of France in a hopeless position, precariously suspended between the devil of unqualified surrender to the new order and the deep sea of flight.

Louis chose the latter course. He fled from Paris to St. Cloud. But the people brought him back, and when he tried to escape again, this time to Metz, he and his family were ignominiously stopped at Varennes. Back in Paris he was forced into a declaration of loyalty and had to pledge that he would uphold the Constituent Assembly. France still wanted its king, but a king whose status would be changed from monarch to virtual prisoner.

Now a short period of calm set in. The Revolution lay spread across the land like a giant resting to renew his strength. But suddenly the giant stirred. The breathing space was over. Danton the champion had begun to prepare the minds of the people for a Republic; Robespierre's roar echoed in the Jacobin Club; and at the miniature Court of Coblenz, outside the borders of France, the émigrés, by their conduct and their clamor to for-

eign powers to stem the flow of the Revolution, were adding
fuel to the fires of passion.

And then, though France was sorely unprepared for hostilities,
Louis and his Girondin ministry declared war on Austria in the
spring of 1792. Everywhere the French armies suffered calami-
tous defeat. Disaster followed disaster and served to rouse the
anger of the mob against the king and even more violently
against the queen. The Court Party was denounced; the queen
was abused and vilified. She was the "Austrian woman," the arch-
traitress, perfidious and wicked, whose treachery in favor of the
land of her birth had brought misfortune to the arms of France.
Down with the Austrian woman, howled the mob! Down with
treason and faithlessness! In a mighty wave the yelling sans-culottes stormed the Tuileries. Like an immense pack of hungry
wolves they surged about the defenseless king, raving and scoff-
ing and threatening him with the strange sharp weapons with
which they were armed. They stuck the Red Cap of Liberty
upon his head. . . . The Revolution was making itself master
of France. But on this day Louis and Marie Antoinette, his queen,
"poor dupes of the vehement needs of the times," won their last
victory for the monarchy. For it was by their royal dignity and
courage that they saved their lives.

II

All this while Catherine Grand was still making concessions
to the spirit of the times. She was living now in a house in the
Rue Mirabeau under the protection of a wealthy nobleman of
the Faubourg Saint-Germain, the dashing Vicomte de Lambertye.
She had a fine house, elegant furniture, jewels, and money
enough. Shrewdly, however, she displayed little of her wealth.
She dressed simply, lived quietly, and never appeared abroad in
her carriage. Her practical common sense gave her the wisdom
of discretion. In these troublesome times it was sound policy to
emulate the chameleon, particularly for one who had been so

conspicuous a member of gay society as this notorious courtesan. True, no one could accuse her of the crime of noble birth, but there was no denying her association with the nobility and the higher bourgeoisie, or her wealth.

Day by day as Paris grew more and more dangerous for people like Catherine Grand and her high-born protector, the fingers of fear tightened about her heart. Yet when Lambertye fled to England soon after the Declaration of Pilnitz, she refused to accompany him. Despite her growing anxiety, she chose to remain in the city she loved. She did, however, take three further precautions for her welfare—she packed a great many of her possessions like one about to set out on a journey, she had her coach repaired so that it would be ready for use should she require it for sudden flight, and she sublet part of her house to a loyal and worthy citizen of the middle class named Amalin. But in spite of this last measure to ward off suspicion and show good faith, her house was searched by the Committee of the Section of Mirabeau early in May, exactly eighteen days after Citizen Amalin had moved into one part of it. The Committee discovered nothing but her possessions. An inventory of these was made. It was a lengthy process. The contents of one trunk only—a collection of silver and gold-plated coffeepots, teapots, pepperpots, candlesticks, tea caddies, sugar tongs, forks, spoons, dishes, and salvers—were worth a small fortune. So were her furs. One cupboard alone contained eleven pieces of mink's tail, seven strips of martin's tail, a tippet of blue fox, and a muff of silver fox. The searchers adjourned to her library. Carefully they inspected her books and wrote down the titles in a long list. There they found the *Histoire de Prusse* by M. de Mirabeau, the *Voyage d'Anacharsis,* the *Chevalier de Faublas,* the *Contes* of Boccaccio and those of Voltaire, the works of Jean Jacques Rousseau, the *Fables* of La Fontaine, a "Boileau in two volumes bound in red morocco, by Didot," the *Pucelle d'Orléans,* the *Henriade,* the *Entretiens du Palais-Royal,* a collection of songs, and the *Femme vertueuse. . . .* At last the search was over. The Committee of the Section of Mirabeau had done its work. Nothing had been discovered to arouse suspicion and the investigators departed. Alone once more Catherine Grand stood pale and trembling. Alarm bells of warning clanged in her heart.

Still she would not forsake Paris. The days passed and now in her ears the low mutterings of the sans-culottes sounded like the moan of the sea when the tide comes in. The mutterings grew in volume till they rose to yells and raving howls as, on June 20th, the mob rushed into the Tuileries to mock and taunt and menace a weak, defenseless king, suddenly grown strong with a strange calm dignity and courage. That day, filled with dread, Catherine rushed out to buy forty-six ells of tricolor ribbon from Citizen Boucon, purveyor of ribbons and scarves to the municipality. Busily she set about turning the narrow strips of silk into rosettes and bows so that she might wear tricolor cockades conspicuously on her breast and in her hair.

III

From Paris the Revolution had spread to the far corners of France. Everywhere the seeds of civil war began to push their heads above the ground. Danton was the man of the moment; the voice of Maximilien Robespierre rang loudly through the Jacobin ranks; and on the road from Marseilles sounded the tramp of feet as a crowd of young men came swinging along to the beat of a new marching song. Soon after they had reached the gates of Paris everyone was singing their ditty. The workmen of the southeastern section of the city gave the tune a name. They called it the *Marseillaise*.

Prussia had joined Austria and declared war on France, and now from Coblenz the Duke of Brunswick, Commander of the allied armies, issued a manifesto to the French people—a document Louis of France had asked of his Germanic friends but which, undoubtedly, he had never dreamed would be worded with such monstrous insolence. The manifesto commanded the people of France to submit unequivocally to their legitimate

sovereign; exhorted them "not to oppose themselves to the march
and operations" of the allied troops; and warned them that "if
the least assault be perpetrated against the King and Queen and
the Royal Family" the forces of Prussia and Austria "would
take an exemplary and never-to-be-forgotten vengeance by giving up the town of Paris to military execution and to total sub-
version." That fatal manifesto sealed the doom of Louis XVI.

*De l'audace, encore de l'audace, toujours de l'audace, et la
France est sauvée,* ran Danton's motto—words that were taken
up by Robespierre, Marat, Desmoulins and the Paris mob, and
went echoing through the length and breadth of the land, fo-
menting insurrection.

On August 25, 1792, Catherine ordered "a Greek chemise of
gray taffeta shot with green." It was paid for and delivered almost immediately—this cloak most suitable for a lady preparing
for a long journey. . . . But the storm broke before she had
quite made up her mind to flee. On the calm starlit night of
August 9th the gale of insurrection which Danton had been
raising with his speeches broke over the roofs of Paris. All night
the tocsins sounded. The people were slow to assemble, and
meanwhile in the Gardens of the Tuileries the king, who had
gathered six thousand men about him, stood waiting anxiously.
"When will the revolt begin?" he kept asking Roederer repeatedly. "When will the revolt begin?"

But when it began it was not a revolt. It was the Deluge
which Louis XIV had prophesied. . . . The mob entered the
Carrousel; it stormed the Tuileries. The garrison was killed; the
Swiss Guard, fighting valiantly, retreated through the Gardens,
and the king and his royal family fled to the Riding School and
then onward to seek refuge in the Assembly.

Roused to demoniacal fury, the sans-culottes poured like mol-
ten lava through the streets. In a wild and frenzied orgy they
sacked and pillaged as they went. Maddened by the heroic and
loyal devotion of the Swiss Guard at the Tuileries, they massa-
cred every Swiss who came within reach of their murderous
arms. Not one was spared. Not even the porter of Catherine

Grand's house in the Rue Mirabeau. From a window high up beneath the roof she saw him horribly murdered before her terrified eyes. Now her cup of fear ran over. The next day, when the monarchy was suspended and Louis and his royal family were sent as prisoners to the Temple, and a great terror came to rule in place of the king, she fled precipitately from Paris.

Chapter Six

I

Wrapped in a long cloak, Catherine Grand sat with her head pillowed on her maid's bosom as the packet for Dover, which carried her from France, crept across the English Channel. Dizziness and nausea, added to overwhelming fatigue, sent her at times into a state bordering on semiconsciousness. She longed for forgetfulness of the terrors that racked her mind at the awful knowledge of her plight. She felt desperately ill. One moment waves of heat burned her aching limbs, the next, a cold sweat bathed her body. She wept helplessly.

Hours passed. Tortured with fever and fatigue she fell asleep at last. Then suddenly she was awake again. Excited voices were about her. Someone beside her cried loudly: "See, there it is, the English coast." She opened her eyes, troubled with fever and anxiety. Dumbly she stared into her maid's face. The woman smiled. "Would you not like to see it too, the English coast?" she asked gently. "There is sunlight falling on it, madame."

"Sunlight?" said Catherine wonderingly.

With the maid's help she rose to her feet and walked to the ship's side. There, leaning against the rail, she stood listlessly staring at the white chalk cliffs of Dover that loomed out of grayblue hazy veils of distance. Cool and refreshing the salt spray fell on her burning cheeks. She threw back her head and inhaled the sharp tang of the sea.

"You are feeling a little better, madame?" asked the maid.

"I don't know. It is as if I were living in a nightmare. Nothing seems real but the weariness of my body."

"But you will soon be well again, madame. There in England, where the sun shines on the cliffs, we shall find peace and happiness."

"Happiness?" said Catherine. "But we are alone. What will become of us?"

"The Vicomte de Lambertye—"

"Shall we ever find him again, do you think? . . . So alone, so friendless," she said. Then, suddenly, sharply, she asked: "How much money have we with us?"

The maid fumbled with a purse. In silence she showed its contents cupped in the palm of her hand. Catherine touched the coins one by one. "Twelve louis."

"Ah, but, madame, we have our lives. We are safe."

"Safe? Yes, yes, safe, my friend, and penniless in a strange land." Catherine looked across the narrow strip of sea that stretched between her and the strange land. She saw trees and grassy slopes and tiny thatched cottages and Dover Castle clear-cut against the sky. And she wept again, pitifully.

On the quay where she sat half-conscious in her maid's arms, a young man saw her, a young man who wore the uniform of a British midshipman. Never had he seen so lovely a lady so distressed and ill. Her beauty bewitched him. Suddenly it seemed to him that he was no longer a young naval cadet but a hero of some ancient fable, the youngest son of the fairy tale whose duty it was to rescue beautiful princesses from the cruel ogres. In this spirit he approached Catherine, told her his name, Nathaniel Belchier, and offered her his services. Because he was kind and sympathetic and gallant, she told him her story—how she had once lived in India and had there married an Englishman; how she had left India because of her unhappiness and before obtaining a divorce from her husband; and how now she had fled from France, leaving all her property behind in Paris.

"But if you are still a British subject, madame," said Belchier, "you have a right to claim your property from the French Government."

"A right? But I am so tired, so tired," she answered. Her eyes suddenly dilated with terror. "My porter, the Swiss. They murdered him beneath my windows. . . . They were slaughtering innocents. And I grew afraid and ran away. But I had done nothing treacherous, do you understand, nothing unpatriotic. I was only afraid."

Nathaniel Belchier's glance never left her face, that pale, beautiful oval face set in its frame of golden hair. He felt half drunk with admiration and daring.

"They were like hungry wolves," he heard her whisper. "Hungry wolves. And I fled from Paris, my maid and I. I scarcely know how we reached the coast of France. I was barely alive. My maid, this good and faithful creature, saved us both. But now that we are here, I do not know what will become of us. We have no papers. This is all we possess." She opened her purse and he saw the few poor coins. In that instant he felt that he had but one mission in life—to help her. He said gravely: "Madame, if you will allow me, I shall recover your possessions."

"But they are in France, monsieur! In France!" she repeated.

"I know, madame, and it is from France that I mean to bring them."

"But why should you do this dangerous thing for me, a stranger, washed up on the shores of England?"

"Because, madame," he answered seriously, "by rendering a small service to the loveliest lady I have ever seen, I wish to satisfy my own deep selfishness."

Tears welled up in her eyes. "You would risk your life for me?" she asked.

"If by doing so I could bring happiness to yours, madame"— and he bowed.

Late that evening the Dover coach took Catherine Grand, accompanied by her maid and Nathaniel Belchier, to London. The young midshipman attended to her welfare, saw her safely installed in comfortable lodgings, and then sought out his best friend, a young gentleman named O'Dryer. Graphically he related his story. O'Dryer was an eager listener and ready for any adventure. So it happened that a few days later they set out for Paris with full power "to act for Madame Grand in the recovery of the property she had left there." Difficulties and dangers assailed them, but they overcame them all and three months later arrived back in London with their mission successfully achieved. Into Catherine's hands they placed the fruits of their romantic venture—gold plate valued at eighty thousand livres, jewels worth three hundred thousand livres, two thousand one hundred louis d'ors in belts about their waists, and a lady disguised in sailor clothes—in short the greater portion of Catherine's property, valued at £25,000, as well as her friend Madame Villemain from Abbéville!

As a token of her gratitude for his great kindness and magnificent daring, Catherine begged Nathaniel Belchier to accept from her a large and generous sum of money. He refused it. He would take only £60 to defray the traveling expenses he and O'Dryer had incurred. No other mode of payment was offered him. Nor did he desire it. "I call the gods to witness that my one aim and wish was to succor a sick and sorely distressed Royalist lady of of the most wondrous and astonishing beauty," he hotly rebuked the bloods of the day who dared to chaff him about his reward. "I repeat, sirs, I desired no compensation, no compensation of any kind."

II

During the autumn and winter of this year, the trend and flow of the French Revolution and the grueling adventures of the émigrés who were pouring into the country in great numbers, formed almost the only topics of conversation in England. Daily and by divers ways the fugitives arrived. The more fortunate ones crossed the Channel by the Brighton and Dover packets; others, who had escaped imprisonment and death only by fleeing in open boats, were brought to safety by English fishermen searching for lobsters close to the French coast.

London was full of refugees, and in the country districts near the metropolis the unhappy strangers formed themselves into small settlements. Madame de Genlis, onetime mistress of Philip Égalité, Duke of Orléans, and governess to his children, gathered a coterie of followers about her at Bury; Madame de

Broglie hired a cottage at West Humble; another group of fugitives settled at Richmond, and yet another, the most famous of all, rented Juniper Hall, close to the home of Fanny Burney's sister Susanna Phillips, in the Vale of Mickleham.

"There can be nothing imagined more charming, more fascinating than this colony," Fanny Burney wrote in a letter to her father at this time. "Between their sufferings and their *agréments* they occupy us almost wholly."

The Marquise de la Châtre, Monsieur de Jaucourt, the Princess d'Hénin, de Lally-Tollendal, Monsieur d'Arblay, who had been Lafayette's adjutant and who succumbed to Fanny's charms, the *ci-devant* duc de Montmorency, and Narbonne, until recently Constitutionalist Minister of War to His Majesty of France, were all members of this coterie of noblesse of whom, just before the end of January, Madame de Staël became the ruling queen. Many guests visited the colony at Juniper Hall, but after Madame de Staël's arrival none came more frequently than a certain limping gentleman with a snakelike smile and strange glittering eyes. He was Charles Maurice de Talleyrand, the excommunicated Bishop of Autun. Old Horace Walpole called him "the viper that has cast his skin."

"How do you like him?" whispered Madame de Staël to Fanny Burney on the day of his first appearance at Juniper Hall.

"Not very much," she answered. "But then, I do not know him."

"Oh, I assure you, he is the best of men," came the forceful assurance.

Not everyone felt so vehement an admiration for Monsieur de Talleyrand as Madame de Staël, yet he had a strange fascination even for those who despised him for his treachery and venality. There was wizardry in Talleyrand's personality. He had the ability to hide the gross garments of his unscrupulousness, profligacy, and faithlessness with astonishing *sangfroid* beneath a cloak of dignity, courtliness, wit, and eloquence. Such was the power of this man that, notwithstanding his physical unattractiveness, his lack of principles, honor, and moral prestige, he captivated many men and most women by the brilliance of his mind and the charm of his manners. Even prim Fanny Burney, with her preconceived prejudices, fell under his spell soon after their first meeting. "It is inconceivable what a convert Talleyrand has made of me," she wrote and told her father. "I think him now one of the first members and one of the most charming of this exquisite set. Susanna (Mrs. Phillips) is completely a proselyte. His powers of entertainment are astonishing, both in information and raillery."

III

Charles Maurice de Talleyrand belonged to one of the oldest and noblest families in France, the Talleyrand-Périgords. When he was a small child an accident rendered him lame for life and, since so great a family deemed it imperative to have at its head a physically sound and perfect man, Talleyrand was deprived of his rights as eldest son of the house in favor of his younger brother, the Comte d'Archambault. But what was to become of the limp-foot? Well, for such a one there was always the Church. So the cripple was educated at the Séminaire de St. Sulpice and at the Sorbonne and in the flower of his youth was forced into the Church.

He had a violent dislike for the profession that had been foisted on him and made no secret of his disinclination for the priesthood. Early in life he determined to use both it and his great name purely as stepping-stones to his ambition. He wanted to be a statesman, a diplomat. Even as a student he cultivated the friendship only of those who would prove helpful to him in the achievement of his overweening desire for political power and riches. As a young man he frequented the salon of Madame du Barry. It was she who first brought him to the notice of the King. This young priest of noble birth and outstanding ability, whose charm and wit were already coupled with the most flagrant immorality, became agent-general of the French clergy at the age of twenty-six; at thirty-five he was created Bishop of Autun and elected a member of the States-General which, after one hundred and seventy-five years, met at Versailles in 1789.

Talleyrand's career as a great statesman may be said to date from this fateful day in May. Now he turned to support the popular leaders and soon became the most prominent figure in the Assembly after Mirabeau. As his political career passed from brilliance to greater brilliance, his defiance of the Church increased. In the end he was excommunicated by the Pope. This was no great blow to the ambitious young man. Rather did he look upon it as a happy release. The cloak of the Bishop of Autun had served its purpose. Now at last he was plain Monsieur de Talleyrand, diplomat.

In January 1792, he accompanied Chauvelin to England in the capacity of unofficial ambassador. Strict orders had been entrusted to him. He was to persuade George III into a declaration of neutrality so that "the English fleet would not attack the French coasts while the armies of continental Europe were invading their frontiers." In this mission Monsieur Chauvelin's limping Minister Plenipotentiary of extraordinary charm and epigrammatic wit was eminently successful. Unfortunately, at the height of his success, the Revolution in France renewed itself and terror swept in with the tide. When the mob loudly bawling the sinister *Ça ira* stormed the Tuileries on June 20th, England turned suspicious eyes on Talleyrand, and he promptly took his departure for Paris. He arrived to find a chaos of anarchy. Everywhere he heard himself called "the half-caste patriot." The Royalists looked on his recent mission to England with mistrust, the Jacobins suspected him of intrigues with the loathsome "Austrian Committee." Undaunted, he watched events from behind the barrier of his reserve, changed his principles "according to the wind of the day," and fixed his eyes on Danton, because Danton was the man of the moment. And when the monarchy fell and Danton became Minister of Justice, it was the polished, profligate ex-Bishop of Autun whom he chose as one of his counsellors.

But now, as excess followed excess and the extremists gradually gained power, Talleyrand grew restless. The mob with its cruelty and bestiality terrified him. At all costs he would escape its clutches. "Leave Paris," he advised all his friends, "leave Paris." Graphically he painted the horrors that were to come. Hastily, secretly, they left, those terrified refugees of the Revolution. Talleyrand, too, wanted to leave, but not in illegal flight like an émigré. He wished to keep the doors of France open behind him in case he should soon desire to return. By intrigue and skillful trickery and by clinging to Danton like a limpet, he at last managed to obtain the document which legally let him out of France. "Pass Charles Maurice de Talleyrand going to London by our orders," ran the passport which Danton himself had signed.

So, a few months after he had left as Chauvelin's Minister Plenipotentiary, Talleyrand was back in London again. Some believed that he had come on a secret mission, but to Lord Grenville he said: "I am anxious that you should know that I have absolutely no mission of any kind in England and have only come here to seek peace and enjoy liberty among its real friends." He went to live quietly in Woodstock Street, and there for a time the Comtesse de Châtre kept house for him. He spent many hours each day with Madame de Flahaut in Half Moon Street and corrected the proofs of her latest novel; he became one of the "first members" of the brilliant colony of refugees who had settled at Juniper Hall.

It was the execution of Louis XVI and Marie Antoinette that sealed Talleyrand's fate in England and brought his stay to an end. "Monsieur de Talleyrand was a deep and dangerous man." He had been the President of the Constituent Assembly that had organized the awful Revolution which England so deeply hated and condemned. True, despite his earlier carefulness to leave France only with a passport, he had recently been declared an émigré by the Convention. But did that mean anything? One never knew what Talleyrand had up his sleeve. He was treacherous and deceitful. There was only one way of dealing with such a man. Pitt expelled him from England. On March 2, 1794, Charles Maurice de Talleyrand turned his back on Europe and set sail for the land of liberty, the United States of America.

IV

Meanwhile Catherine Grand, her fortune restored to her by the gallantry and daring of Nathaniel Belchier and safely stored in the vaults of the Bank of England, was living quietly in London, quietly because, in view of the sobering effect that the fierce revolutionary events in France were having on English society, she deemed it wise to portray herself as an émigrée of impeccable propriety of conduct. Yet despite her decorum the drawing room doors of the great were not opened to her. English society, with its prudish regard for social morals, was suspicious of Madame Grand and regarded her with the same stiff, snobbish disapproval with which it viewed the libertinism of the gay set that the Prince of Wales, "with his appetite for pleasure and a head for foibles," had gathered about him.

Sternly, however, Catherine clung to her role of respectability. With no desire to be led off the path of propriety, she refrained even from informing Philip Francis of her presence in London. Then one day, quite by accident, they met. Catherine's decorous retirement came to an end. Gradually she drifted into that set which held determinedly aloof from the stiff snobbishness of court society, that set to which the daring Duchess of Devonshire lent so much grace, and to which Fox and Sheridan belonged.

At this time Catherine had made the acquaintance of vivacious Bet Armistead who had once been London's most prominent woman of the town and who "knew more men and knew them better than any woman of her day." Once she had numbered the Prince of Wales, Lord Derby, and the Duke of Dorset among her lovers. Now, though brilliant wits and men of fashion still gathered about her, she gave them only friendship. Her love and loyal devotion belonged to Charles Fox for all time. Catherine often went to visit her at Chertsey, St. Anne's Hill. There the easily moved Fox, "whose mind was impervious to social distinctions," welcomed her warmly and introduced her to his coterie of friends who, like himself, were unpopular in England because of their sympathy with and understanding of the French Revolution.

But besides Philip Francis and the people at Chertsey—of whom, incidentally, Francis greatly disapproved, for he and Fox were at daggers drawn—Catherine had many other friends, Englishmen as well as émigrés. Nathaniel Belchier was still gallant and courtly; with the Vicomte de Lambertye she went to concerts at the Pantheon and to watch Mrs. Siddons act at Sadlers Wells. And one fine day she met Cristofero Spinola, a diplomat from the Republic of Genoa whose father-in-law, the Maréchal de Lévis, had lost his head in the Terror. During the last months of her residence in England Spinola, with whom she had been on friendly terms for some time, became her lover.

But Juniper Hall, with its great cedars and spacious lawns so much beloved by Monsieur de Talleyrand and Madame de Staël, remained forever an unknown world to Catherine Grand.

Chapter Seven

I

"Louis must die because the country must live," cried Robespierre. And Louis died, protesting to the end that he had never in his life desired anything but good for his people. Nine months later Marie Antoinette, his queen, gave up her life proudly, as befitted the daughter of Maria Theresa. The Reign of Terror with its bloodshed and slaughter had begun. Marat was murdered by Charlotte Corday in retaliation for the overthrow of the Gironde, and in the Place de la Révolution Madame la Guillotine did her mundane work quickly and horribly to the music of rattling tumbrils. "To be safe," said Hébert, "you must kill everybody."

Then Danton and Robespierre overwhelmed the Hébertists and had them guillotined. But when the moderates tried to check the course of bloodshed, Robespierre resolved to free himself from his allies by violence, and on April 8, 1794, Danton and Desmoulins and their followers dropped their heads into a basket. Robespierre, egoist and arch-terrorist, and his Triumvirate were now supreme. In every village and town in France blood flowed in streams as the sharp ax of the guillotine descended on the necks of its victims. In Paris alone, within three months, three thousand people met death at the hands of the Revolutionary Tribunal. . . . Then the sickle of retribution mowed down the great Robespierre himself and his bloodlusting comrades, for the masses, surfeited with horrors, had risen up against the harsh oppression of tyranny.

But though Robespierre was brought to his end, the guillotine for a time continued its awesome work, and the gilded youth of Paris, their hair arranged *à la victime,* still rushed along the boulevards pursuing their enemies with the old cry of Liberty.

But at last the Terror passed. The Jacobins were overthrown and those of the Girondists who remained were summoned once again to take their seats in the Convention. Out of this Convention the Directory was born, the Directory of which Barras was the virtual dictator. Paris became gay once more. Though the poor suffered hunger and cold, the *bals des victimes* proved a great success, and the theaters were packed night after night. The Gardens of the Tuileries again became a favorite place of promenade, and women wore their hair cropped *à la sacrifice,* and covered their shoulders with a red shawl to commemorate the red chemise of Charlotte Corday.

Madame la Guillotine no longer cast her spectral shadow across France. The Revolution was over, its object achieved. Gone were ancient traditions, old forms of government, the old state of society. A new era had come with new influences, new customs, and new manners. Madame Tallien, who had been Theresia Cabarrus, was the queen of Paris, and "a young, pale, sickly-looking" artillery officer, a Corsican named Napoleon Bonaparte, hero of the October rising, came from the third-rate inn where he was living to attend parties in Barras' salon.

II

With the Terror over and the Directory firmly established, France beckoned once again to Catherine Grand. She longed for Paris, that strangely changed Paris where Theresia Tallien and Josephine Beauharnais, women like herself, were proclaimed the leaders of fashion and society. Cristofero Spinola's thoughts, too, had turned to France, for in France he hoped to retrieve or to gain compensation for the property of his father-in-law who had perished during the blood fever of the Revolution. So Catherine Grand and Cristofero Spinola planned to make the journey across the Channel together.

It was not easy for an émigrée to reenter France. But Catherine no longer feared for her head. With nostalgia quickening her pulses, she was ready to strike down every obstacle on her road to Paris. She boldly approached the Danish minister in England and begged him to issue her a passport. She told him her story. It was a difficult case, said the Danish minister. Why had she come to him since she was the wife of a Swiss who had become a British national? Had he forgotten that she had been born in a Danish settlement in India, in Tranquebar? She cajoled as only Catherine could. She wept a little and looked lovelier than ever. Surely, surely the Danish minister could not find it in his heart to be cruel and refuse her so insignificant a request? . . . And he could not. She *was* too beautiful. Catherine secured her passport, a passport under a false name, and, in the company of Cristofero Spinola, left England for Hamburg. Hamburg was full of French Royalists, chiefly Orléanists, impatiently waiting to slip back into France at the first propitious moment. Madame de Genlis was there and so was Madame de Flahaut. Among this gathering of émigrés Catherine found many old friends and in a few weeks made a host of new acquaintances. Then one day she met a man with a pale face and a rich deep voice. He was dignified, extremely courteous, and very witty. He was Monsieur de Talleyrand, the limping ex-Bishop of Autun, who had recently returned from America.

III

In the country of Benjamin Franklin, and "in contemplating the imposing spectacle of a free people," Talleyrand had waited for France once more to open her doors to him. Madame de Staël, back again in Paris, had kept him well informed of the turn of events while she worked with all her might to get his name struck off the list of émigrés. Just when he had become so weary of his place of exile that he contemplated sailing for the West Indies, her efforts met with success. The edict of banishment was withdrawn. "So the business is ended, thanks to you," he wrote to her from America. "You have done everything that I desired. . . . It is to your house that I shall come on my arrival. . . . Dear friend, I love you with all my heart."

He set sail from America in a Danish brig on June 13, 1796, and arrived in Hamburg at the end of July. The place was full of his friends and they welcomed him with pleasure and delight —all except his former mistress, Madame de Flahaut. She had become deeply enamored of Monsieur de Souza, the Portuguese minister, and had made up her mind to marry him. The prospect of Talleyrand's sudden arrival sent her into a fever. Fearing that this specter of the past would ruin her plans for the future, she hastily dispatched to him a message that combined cunning artlessness and gentle flattery, suggesting that he refrain from coming ashore and return to America immediately. Needless to say, Talleyrand did not take the slightest notice of this communication. He landed. After spending a month in Hamburg with his friends, he departed for Amsterdam and Brussels. Quietly, on September 26, 1796, he arrived in Paris. Quietly, too, in the following year, the fifth year of the Republic, Catherine Grand, whom he had met one day in Hamburg, slipped across the German border into France.

BOOK V

Questa Donna

Chapter One

I

On a day when the summer sun drew the heat in waves from cobblestones and dank doorways, when the Seine, gliding beneath its bridges, took on the appearance of a stream of aluminum, Catherine Grand once again entered the city she loved. As she sat staring through the window of the carriage that brought her to Paris, tears covered her cheeks. This was the Paris she had left almost five years ago, this dilapidated city with its shabby, crumbling houses, its shattered monuments, and abandoned churches. These were the fashionable faubourgs that she had once known, these impoverished suburbs where grass grew in the untidy streets. All the riches and the glory, the ceremony and pomp, had disappeared. Gone—all gone. The grand places of the mighty had been converted into pleasure saloons for the people; the hôtels of the *haut-ton* now housed dissolute gambling dens; the churches that had not been destroyed were being used as warehouses and dance halls; and monasteries had become barracks. Catherine wept for the splendors of the past that had disappeared from the capital of France.

But though she found Paris outwardly much defiled and sadly altered, she soon discovered that it was as gay a city as ever, with a new, wanton, dissipated gaiety. The sullen thunder of the Revolution had died away into silence, the Terror was gone and, in direct reaction to agony and fear, the pendulum had swung to frenzied revelry and unbridled licence. Amusement and enjoyment had become the fundamental desires of every man and woman. Gaming and dancing were reckoned among the major interests of life. To the churches, convents, monasteries, and palaces which this new era had converted into dancing saloons came the eager *citoyennes,* their hair cut short and curled in supposed resemblance to an ancient Roman fashion, scanty muslin gowns exposing their bare legs, flat sandals on their feet, and rings on their toes. Almost as strangely attired were their escorts, men who wore their clothes deliberately ill-cut in deference to fashion's dictates, hats pulled low over their brows, and necks swathed in enormous cravats that covered their chins and bordered their lower lips.

No longer were there gatherings of friends in little intimate groups and friendly cliques, for such gatherings were looked upon with suspicion by the police since they might well harbor conspirators against the power of the Directory. With spies and plotters everywhere, it was deemed wiser that Paris should live its life publicly and in the open, at the theaters, at fetes, in the gardens, and at subscription balls. Blood no longer held rank; the former monseigneur rubbed shoulders in the great assemblies with parvenu speculators; ladies of good birth and the butcher's wife, reduced to equality by the all-embracing designation of citizeness, danced together in the same quadrille. In all things but one these people were alike—and this one was manners. For manners were the only real social distinction that still remained.

In this Paris to which Catherine had returned after an absence of four years, many outward forms of the Revolution were still being observed. Pet dogs were carefully trained to growl at the mention of an aristocratic name; the revolutionary jargon was still being used as well as the new calendar, and every tenth day was an excuse for a gala celebration. As the old rulers had given way to the new in the realms of government, so too in society new leaders filled the places once occupied by the great ladies of the past, now either dead or fled to foreign lands. The five foremost feminine principals of society were Theresia Tallien, daughter of the once impoverished adventurer Cabarrus; Madame Hamelin; brilliant Madame de Staël who had returned from exile in England with the establishment of the Directory; the beautiful and witty Madame Récamier; and Josephine Bonaparte, wife of a young Corsican general fighting on the Italian front. Josephine's first husband General Beauharnais had met his death at the hands of the Revolutionary Tribunal. Theresia Tallien, mistress of Head Director Barras, was the real queen of this new society—exotic Theresia who drove through the streets in a wine-colored carriage and not only set the fashion of scantiness in modish feminine attire but also in post-revolutionary manners.

In this altered city already talking excitedly of the military genius of young General Bonaparte, and as yet unaware of the talent of a red-haired priest named Fouché living with his wife, an ugly ex-nun, in the abject poverty of a garret, Catherine struggled to readjust herself to a new life. She tried desperately, but it was a heartbreaking business. Most of her friends, among them the Vicomte de Lambertye, were émigrés in foreign lands; many, like poor Valdec Delessart, had perished in the Terror. Only a mere handful of acquaintances from her old life were left in or had returned to Paris, and even these she dared not visit often. Spies and detectives were everywhere, waiting like vultures to pounce on suspected Royalists or those in league with émigrés abroad. She was anxious not to attract the attention of the police. In London and Hamburg she had been in close association with those despised Royalists who had quitted France during the Revolution, and she had managed to reenter Paris by a back door, and under a false name. Small wonder that she chose to live quietly, almost in semiretirement, in a modestly furnished *hôtel* which she rented in the Rue Saint-Vicaise; small wonder that she was frightened and rather sad and often very lonely.

II

"I swear by all the gods that I have lost all taste for public life and that nothing on earth can induce me to meddle with it again." Thus had Monsieur de Talleyrand, former Bishop of Autun, remarked to Madame de Genlis in Hamburg. This high-sounding pledge might have altered the career of any man but Charles Maurice de Talleyrand. To him, however, whose vows of celibacy formed no barrier to the enchantments of the fair sex and whose sophistries could allay any pricks of conscience, the breaking of such a resolution was a minor matter. In all things he was the perfect opportunist, riding roughshod over every rule of behavior and morality that barred the road to success.

The Paris that Catherine found so depressing was at first in no way encouraging to Monsieur de Talleyrand, though his return had caused a considerable stir. His wit was remembered by many a lady who had known him in the days of the old regime. Talleyrand, who used women as stepping-stones to success, wasted no time in reconquering them with his brilliance and his courtesies. Madame de Staël in particular soon had his bons mots reechoing through the Paris salons. She was his excellent friend. It was through her instigation that his name was struck off the roll of émigrés. Like a limpet to a rock he now adhered to her, for he could be most tender and ardent where his personal advantage was concerned. He bound himself with veritable hoops of steel to those who could be of use to him. So now, since he had a great temporary need of Madame de Staël, he clung to her. She was a friend of Barras, head of the government of France, a government so powerful that the crafty former Bishop of Autun had no objection to serving it.

Step by step, in the salon of Madame de Staël, this brilliant, profligate priest who owed the start of his public career to an improper joke about the immorality of Paris made in the drawing room of Madame du Barry, carefully planned his return to the political arena of a new France under the Directory. Cold, polished, ambitious for wealth and power, and with one all-consuming passion, that of self-interest, he used finesse and the men and women who were his friends—particularly the women —to gain his end. Like a mole, warily, he worked underground, scheming, intriguing, planning. Steadily, through sheer force of intellect and judgment, he made his way to the surface.

France had not forgotten that Talleyrand had been a friend of Mirabeau, nor that he had been President of the Constituent Assembly which had organized the Revolution. The mass of the Convention were not opposed to having a former grand seigneur in their company and the grand seigneurs who were still in France decided that it would be an excellent thing for them if one of their own spirit got into power. Unfortunately the Directorate as a whole, though fully aware of Monsieur de Talleyrand's liberal views and of the fact that his hands were unpolluted by the blood of the Terror, looked askance at him. They were afraid of him, afraid of his brilliance, his cunning, and his treachery. But Madame de Staël was determined to make a minister of her friend, and she cleverly set about winning Barras over to her way of thinking. "My devotion to you is unchangeable," she wrote to Barras on one occasion, "and it alone has made me conceive the idea of becoming useful to you. . . . I am associated with a man whom you already know and who shares my feelings. He is a man of solid genius, bold but prudent. We are both determined to follow your fortunes. . . ."

When there was a rumor of a change in the Ministry she took Talleyrand with her one night when she called on the head of the Directorate. The interview was not a success. Physically Talleyrand reminded Barras too much of Robespierre. He had the same stiff, unbending manner, the same hard mouth and glittering eyes, the same high protruding cheekbones and tilted nose. Suddenly, too, Barras thought of Mirabeau. Talleyrand, the grand seigneur, once Bishop of Autun, had been Mirabeau's confidential friend, yet Mirabeau had called him "a vile base trickster." One would have to be careful with Talleyrand. He was too clever, too calm, too ostensibly indifferent. True, his ability amounted to genius. It would be difficult to find a diplomat better suited to manage the foreign policy of France. Yet he was treacherous and deceitful. A dangerous man.

In spite of these thoughts Barras broached the matter of Talleyrand's appointment to the Directorate. He was met with a storm of opposition from his colleagues. "This limp-foot without respect for his bishopric," declared one of the Directors, "is like a sponge which sucks up every liquid into which it is dropped, but unlike the sponge, never gives anything back." And Carnot said: "He brings with him all the vices of the old regime without having been able to acquire any of the virtues of the new. He has no fixed principles. He changes them as he does his linen and takes them according to the wind of the day —a philosopher when philosophy is the mode; a Republican now because that is necessary in order to become anything."

Talleyrand, courtier and wit, was not one jot discouraged by the obstacles to be surmounted. For the sake of appearances he did sometimes philosophize about the weariness and poverty of life and its utter hopelessness, and remark that only in death, perhaps, there was peace and quiet. Such disgruntled mutterings he murmured into the sympathetic ears of Madame de Staël. To her, too, he confided that the depths of the Seine were perhaps the best place to quench the fruitless desires of a mortal soul. After all, was not all life fleeting and temporary and therefore, what did it matter if—? Here Monsieur de Talleyrand gave a meaningful shrug.

All this philosophizing did not mean a thing to him, but Madame de Staël, who did not appreciate his macabre humor, took his word for the deed (two things which Talleyrand never confused—each being used for a different purpose), and rushed off to Barras.

"Barras, *mon ami*," she cried, hurrying into his study one night, her hair disordered, a wild look in her eyes. "Barras, he told me he was going to throw himself into the Seine!"

"But who, madame? Who is going to throw himself into the Seine?" demanded Barras.

"I am talking of our poor Talleyrand," she cried. "Ah, *mon Dieu*, perhaps he is no longer alive! He has nothing in the world but ten louis."

"Has he no other resources? No friends?" asked Barras.

"Friends, indeed! I who am certainly his friend have gladly supported him until now. His expenses have been so small. He

has not even hired a carriage since his return. But now—now—"
Madame was on the verge of an attack of convulsions. Foam
flecked her lips. She gripped both Barras' hands with all her
strength. *"Mon ami,* you must make a minister of Talleyrand
or I shall be in despair and kill myself," she cried. "Do this
for me and you shall save us all. I am giving the Republic a
valuable friend in the person of poor Talleyrand and I shall be
answerable for him till death."

Torn between pity for Madame's condition and a sudden
concern for Talleyrand's life, Barras tried to soothe his friend
and in his attempt to allay her fears committed himself to an
indirect pledge. "Persuade your friend not to drown himself,"
were his last words to Madame de Staël, "for if he did it would
no longer be possible to make anything of him. Perhaps we
shall be able to utilize his talents for the Republic."

It was only a half promise, but it was something, and Madame
rushed off to save Talleyrand from the Seine in which he really
never had the slightest intention of drowning himself. But his
trick had worked. He knew now quite positively from which
side the wind was blowing. Calm as ever, his cadaverous face
completely expressionless, he set about pulling strings while
he waited for the apple of power to ripen on its bough. At the
end of August, 1797, the apple dropped into his lap. Talleyrand
was himself again. As a representative of the Directory he took
up his residence in the Hôtel Gallifet, Rue du Bac, the official
home of the Minister of Foreign Affairs. He was an important
man in the Government of France once more, for he had stormed
and captured a key position.

Chapter Two

I

In her shabby gray house with its wrought-iron balconies, life was daily becoming more intolerable for Catherine Grand. Hours of endless monotony were wearing her nerves threadbare and her large blue eyes were often sad. She was desperately worried by the lack of money. True, she did possess a fair fortune, but it was locked away in the vaults of the Bank of England, and she realized only too clearly that to bring it over to France, this new France so greedy and rapacious and mistrustful, would be sheer madness. Also, there were the terrifying persecutions of spies and police. Whenever she thought of them she was filled with sickening dread. They mistrusted everyone, these police. Every time she went out of her house she was aware of being followed. Cristofero Spinola, diplomat of the Republic of Genoa and her very good friend, had told her that he too was being watched. They suspected him, so Spinola believed on good authority, of being an agent of the Englishman Malmesbury. . . . They were everywhere, those prying, cautiously watchful, peering eyes!

The passing weeks brought her no relief from anxiety, in fact, her fears grew in intensity. One evening, alone in her furnished apartments, the wildness of her troubled thoughts drove her into a fever of despair. Though her hands felt hot and clammy she was shivering as she paced restlessly from one end of her drawing room to the other. *Mon Dieu, mon Dieu,* would there never be an end to her misfortunes? And why was the night so still? The silence terrified her. It was so ominous, like an evil thing holding its breath, waiting to strike in the dark. . . . Perhaps down there in the street below her windows, spies were on guard. They were always watching. That very day, walking in the Gardens of the Luxembourg, she had been aware that she was being followed. Were they there again, those spies, watching outside her windows?

Would nothing stem the torrent of her misery? Would there never again be peace and happiness for her? Must she go on suffering loneliness and persecution forever? What if someone, anyone, denounced her to the police? It was easy, that sort of thing. It happened daily. And then—prison. Or perhaps something worse!

She shuddered fearfully. Suddenly she snatched up her cloak, flung it about her shoulders, and rushed out of the room. Two minutes later she was in a cab, hastening to her friend the Marquise de Saint-Croix, sister of Talon, the Attorney General.

II

Monsieur de Montrond was the only guest in the drawing room of the Marquise de Saint-Croix when Catherine, pale and trembling, entered it some time later that evening. As she stepped through the doorway, he was recounting a marvelous tale about the exploits of the heroic General Bonaparte.

"What was it that you were saying of this Bonaparte?" Catherine asked him a few minutes later.

Montrond's wicked little eyes glinted with anticipated amusement as he looked at her anxious face. But he answered in a grave voice. "It is rumored that Bonaparte is about to invade England," he said.

Catherine gasped and grew paler still. "Invade England!" she cried.

"Do not believe him," interrupted Madame la Marquise. "It is only another of Montrond's stories!" She knew that venal roué and his malicious wit only too well. It never disturbed her, but it always distressed Catherine.

Montrond's face was even graver. "No, indeed, it is true, I

assure you. Bonaparte will overrun the whole country from end to end and his soldiers will loot and plunder as they go."

"But the banks, monsieur! The banks will be safe?" Catherine asked.

He chuckled inwardly. So she was worried about her fortune in the English bank? Well, he would tease her a bit. It was an amusing game. She was so ridiculously childlike in her credulity.

In mock horror he threw up his hands. "But, madame, surely you know it is the banks which the soldiers always pillage first," he admonished.

At this, poor, overwrought Catherine's self-control collapsed and she burst into tears. The Marquise de Saint-Croix tried to soothe and control her. "I assure you, *mon amie*, the banks are in no danger. Do not cry. You will only make yourself ill, and truly the whole thing is but one of Montrond's wicked jokes."

But Catherine could not be comforted with mere words. She continued to weep, and in her distress poured out all the grievous anxieties that lay so heavily on her heart. "What can I do? What is there for me to do?" she asked pathetically. "At every step I am watched and persecuted by spies. They do not leave me alone even for a single day. I am in the deepest despair, *mon amie*. In the deepest despair!"

"There seems to be only one thing that you can do," Madame de Saint-Croix advised practically. "Go to Citizen-Minister Talleyrand and tell him everything. He is the only man who can help you."

"Yes, indeed. There is no better thing that Madame Grand can do," chipped in Montrond. "And I, being Talleyrand's best friend, shall give her a note to take to him this very night."

Catherine dried her tears while he wrote his letter. Ten minutes later she was on her way to the Hôtel Gallifet to pay her visit to the Minister of Foreign Affairs. Montrond's malicious little note nestled in the hollow between her breasts.

III

At the conclusion of the debate that evening, Monsieur de Talleyrand had gone to play cards with the Chevalier de Fénélon at that gentleman's house. The game did not go well for Fénélon. He lost heavily but in hopes of regaining his losses forced the play to go on. Even when his pockets were empty, he was still not satisfied.

"Choose anything in this room and I shall stake it against that pin in your cravat," he said to Talleyrand at two o'clock in the morning.

"Anything at all?"

Fénélon nodded.

Talleyrand looked about him. "I should like that," he said, pointing to a small silver urn of delicate workmanship.

Fénélon turned pale. Through trembling lips he muttered dully: "You have chosen the one thing from which I dare not part."

"Ah, well then, let us call the game off," said Talleyrand.

"No!" Fénélon cried out sharply. "The game goes on! We shall play. I stake that thing against your cravat pin."

The Minister of Foreign Affairs shrugged his shoulders and sank back in his chair. The game began. Fénélon lost. Beads of perspiration broke out on his forehead. His hands shook. His breath came in choking sobs. Noticing his distress Talleyrand offered to return the stake that he had lost, but scarcely had the words left his lips when the Chevalier snatched the ornament wildly from his grasp.

"By the Lord! I am a fool," he cried. "I played for nought but the urn. 'Twas the urn I lost, not the contents." With this he tore open the lid, drew a small glass vase from the interior, and violently dashed it to pieces against the mantel. The contents, a fine shower of dark ashes, trickled like sand from a broken hourglass into the fire. In these moments the man seemed half insane. Fearful of displeasing him further, Talleyrand placed the urn under his arm and took his departure.

It was under a light in the Rue de Montpensier that he read the inscription on the urn. "C. H. March 17. Mercy and forgiveness—Miserere," he read. In that instant the gruesome tragedy connected with the urn, which he had completely forgotten, came back to him. How clearly now he remembered everything—the beautiful Countess H., her husband's blinding jealousy and his death, finally, at Fénélon's hands. And then—now he remembered—the lady, in utter hopelessness, had retired to a convent. There she had died. She had left a will and in that will a legacy for her lover. At her request her body was to be opened after death and the heart reduced to ashes and then sent to Fénélon, "so that when he dies it may repose within his coffin, for it is his own."

Greatly distressed by these recollections and filled with grisly horror, Talleyrand hastened on his way. Perplexity and fatigue tormented his mind. He longed for the peace and friendliness of his own rooms. But when he entered the front door of the Hôtel Gallifet he was met by his Swiss servant Joris.

"There is a lady to see you, Citizen-Minister," said Joris.

"At this hour of the morning?" Talleyrand rapped out angrily.

"She has been waiting since ten o'clock, Citizen-Minister. Her business, she says, is of great importance. She has brought with her a letter from Citizen Montrond."

"What is her name?"

"Madame Grand, Citizen-Minister."

"Grand . . . Grand," muttered Talleyrand. Then he remembered. He had met her in Hamburg. A very beautiful woman. Exquisite. . . . But what could she be wanting at the Hôtel of External Relations at this hour? Joris said she had been waiting since ten o'clock. It was now past three. Five mortal hours! . . . Before his all-consuming curiosity, Monsieur de Talleyrand's fatigue and annoyance dissolved like mist at dawn.

"Madame Grand is waiting in the study, Citizen-Minister," said Joris.

IV

The study was silent and shrouded in shadows. Only one light was burning, a rose-shaded lamp that rested on the mantel. In the open doorway Talleyrand stood blinking in the uncertain light. Only after a lapse of several moments did he perceive the figure of a woman seated in a deep armchair before the fire. Walking stiffly with his halting, uncertain gait, he approached her. She did not move. Madame Grand was sound asleep.

Talleyrand's small eyes sparkled amusedly in his thin face. He raised his hand to his mouth and coughed several times, softly. Still Madame did not stir. Wearied by her emotions and the long hours of waiting, she slept peacefully, curled like a kitten in the chair.

Hoping that his movements would wake the lady, Talleyrand fidgeted about the room. He came to the low table on which lay a letter addressed to him. He picked it up, opened it, and stood smiling as he read Montrond's note of introduction. That man was an incorrigible jester. Would his insatiable love for practical jokes never find an end Talleyrand wondered.

Again he turned to look at the sleeping woman. He moved closer and peered down at her, but the hood of the wide cape which almost completely enveloped her figure hid her face from his eyes. He straightened his back and in that instant became aware of Joris standing near the door, on the verge of an explosion of laughter. The novelty of the situation in which his master was placed had proved too much for the servant's sense of humor. Talleyrand stiffened. With a peremptory wave of his hand he dismissed the tittering Swiss. Joris rushed from the room and in his haste to escape slammed the door behind him.

Wakened out of her deep sleep by the noise, Catherine started to her feet in alarm, a cry of terror on her lips. It took her several seconds to collect her senses and to realize where she was.

But suddenly catching sight of Talleyrand, her fear and shock vanished in an instant. With a swift, graceful gesture she threw back her hood. Abashed and smiling tremulously, she stood before him, her face transfused with blushes.

The whole incident was over in a matter of moments, but in those moments Catherine's charming confusion and loveliness produced a curious effect on Monsieur de Talleyrand. This venal, blasé, cynical man of the world, so surfeited with the attachments of brilliant women, felt himself for an instant completely deprived of his self-possession. Almost as confused and embarrassed as she, he stood looking at her, dumb with admiration. He had not remembered that she was so beautiful. The whole picture of her stamped itself indelibly on his senses—her soft, delicately molded features, her unfathomably blue, languishing eyes, her small red mouth, her golden hair falling in curls on her dazzlingly white forehead. . . . The moment passed and Monsieur de Talleyrand recovered himself. He held out his hand and uttered polite, conventional phrases as he led her to a comfortable couch. Seating himself on a low chair at her feet, he begged her to tell him everything that Montrond had but half told in his letter.

"Monsieur, forgive me for my intrusion at this singular hour, but I am in most desperate straits," she began, her eyes filling with tears. "I have such a great need of your help."

"I beg you to confide all your troubles to me, madame, and I shall do whatever is in my power to help you," he assured her.

With a rush of words she related the whole story of her fears and anguish. One moment her eyes were round and innocent as a child's, the next they brimmed over with tears. Never before, thought Talleyrand, had he seen a woman look so lovely when she cried. With gallantry and subtly expressed admiration he comforted her, persuading her to continue the story of her troubles and alarms. Of Montrond's joke concerning Bonaparte's intended invasion of England she spoke with so artless a credulity that he found himself more fascinated than amused by her naïveté.

"You must understand, monsieur, that the greater part of my fortune and the whole of my plate and jewels are lodged in the Bank of England," she told him. "What is to become of me if Bonaparte abandons it to the pillage of his victorious troops as a reward for their valor, and I am left destitute?"

Tearfully and ingenuously she unburdened her sorrows to him. . . . It was scandalous of Montrond to have played such a joke on her! The man was as shameless as the devil and she credulous as a child. She was veritably the dupe of her own terrors, and in that state when one is ready to believe any-thing. . . . But Montrond—that fellow would trip up on his own pranks one day. . . . And yet, the situation was really ridiculously amusing. One could not help chuckling a little at the whole stupid affair. . . .

Madame Grand had come to the end of her story and now, full of ardent solicitousness, he turned to her. "I beg of you to calm your fears, madame, and trust me," he soothed her. Her lips were quivering like those of a child on the verge of tears. He patted her hand consolingly.

"Then you will help me, monsieur?" she asked eagerly.

"I will indeed," he answered with passionate earnestness. "I assure you that no harm will come to you or your fortune. Only trust me."

"Monsieur, I do! Indeed I do! Implicitly!" she cried. "I am most deeply indebted to you and am ever, ever your friend."

Now she smiled. When Catherine smiled through her tears she was lovelier than ever. Talleyrand's cold, selfish, venal heart began to flutter like that of a sleepy hawk. His eyes met hers admiringly. He bent his head and kissed her hand.

But Catherine's mood was, for the moment, more susceptible to his power than to his admiration. Innocently she turned the conversation again to her own perplexed anxieties. Could he not give her some concrete assurance of safety? A letter, for instance? Anxious to please her, and much too gallant to disclose to her that she was the dupe of Montrond's fun, he sat down at his desk and drew up a note of security. It was a preposterous document which assured the safe delivery of her plate and jewels and fortune into the hands of any person she chose to appoint to receive them, in the event of Bonaparte's triumphant army entering the city of London! But Catherine was delighted with it.

Her nerves soothed and her fears allayed, she left the Hôtel Gallifet just before dawn. The absurd letter of security which Talleyrand had so pompously signed and sealed nestled in her bosom. With awe and veneration she thought of Monsieur de Talleyrand, Minister of Foreign Affairs. She suddenly felt happy, for, since he had given her his promise that she would come to no harm, she was no longer afraid.

V

For a long time after she had gone Talleyrand remained in his study, lost in thought. . . . Absurd how that ridiculous security had served to quiet her nerves. Was there ever such an incredibly credulous creature as this Madame Grand! . . . If Montrond's story got about among the wits there would be no end to their laughter. All Paris would be full of the tale. Well, he certainly had played up splendidly to Montrond's joke. . . . *Pardi,* how tantalizingly lovely she was! In this world so full of scheming women like Theresia Tallien and Madame de Staël it was refreshing to meet so simple, ingenuous, and trusting a creature as this Madame Grand. Her unsophisticated sophistication was adorable! . . . He must see more of her. Suddenly he regretted that he had ever embarked on an *affaire de cœur* with Madame Delacroix. She was so mature, and nothing more than merely good-looking. Madame Delacroix could not hold a candle to Catherine Grand.

Dawn was in the sky when Talleyrand at last limped up the long corridor to his bedroom. He was filled with a curious excitement that amused his cynically analytical mind and yet stirred his heart not unpleasantly. For this audacious minister of France, former bishop and profligate roué, who had successfully resisted the alluring wit and refined elegance of many a great lady, now found himself strangely intrigued and fascinated by the beauty and naïveté of a courtesan, by her eyes and her little nose and the scent of her golden hair.

Chapter Three

I

Talleyrand wasted little time before setting off to the Rue Saint-Vicaise to pay his respects to Catherine Grand. The days that followed found him a frequent visitor at her apartment and before long her curiously childlike personality caused the mature charms of Madame Delacroix to pale and lose their meaning for him. Besides, the wife of Charles Delacroix was no longer an asset, and Talleyrand made short work of those who, one way or another, were of no benefit to him.

During the first months after his return to France, in the days when her husband held the office of Minister of Foreign Affairs, Madame Delacroix had been most useful and had served him almost as well as—indeed, in some respects a great deal better than—Madame de Staël. He had become her lover. Madame, though fond enough of her husband, was far from happy in her married life for, unfortunately, Charles Delacroix suffered from a complaint which made it impossible for him to become a father. While she was playing her passionate game with Talleyrand, however, Charles was restored to normal health. But though he regained his health he lost his ministerial office. It was Monsieur de Talleyrand who, in his place, became host at the Hôtel of External Affairs. Six months later Madame presented Charles with a son. At this society tittered scandalously. Only a few staunch friends were filled with silent sympathy for poor Delacroix who had been so summarily displaced by Talleyrand both in the Directorate and his wife's good favor.

But all that had taken place long ago, and much had happened since. Madame Delacroix had served her purpose. After his nocturnal meeting with Catherine Grand, her reign came to an abrupt end. Not only was Catherine far more beautiful than she, but Catherine, he realized, might prove useful to him. Had she not naïvely confessed to a secret correspondence with the Vicomte de Lambertye in London? Besides, she possessed a goodly fortune locked safely in the vaults of the Bank of England and Talleyrand had a great respect for money. So he began to visit the hôtel in the Rue Saint-Vicaise regularly. Occasionally, too, Catherine lunched or dined at the Hôtel Gallifet. Sometimes she stayed the night. In the mornings when she awoke she appeared to him lovelier than ever.

The months passed . . . he rented a house for Catherine at Montmorency. On the ninth day of every ten he went there and stayed until the first day of the next ten. He was very happy there. Because he was not fond of solitude the house was filled with guests. These visitors were carefully selected, and only those who were amusing and harmonious or politically important to Monsieur de Talleyrand were invited. Theresia Tallien and Josephine Bonaparte frequently appeared in the Montmorency drawing room—the one because she was the mistress of Barras, the other because she was the wife of a pale-faced Corsican general whose genius the farsighted former Bishop of Autun had already fully recognized.

Montmorency provided its guests with excellent food and wine and amusing entertainment. Frequently good amateur musicians gave concerts there or actors staged tragedies and farces. Sometimes the evenings were passed in the playing of innocent games for pledges and forfeits. Catherine's favorite blindman's buff held first place in these artless recreations. To please her the wily Citizen-Minister jumped about clumsily on his thin unsteady legs many an evening, his eyes blindfolded but his wits as nimble and crafty as ever. But it was the gambling banks—birribi, roulette, rouge et noir and faro—which were the most popular of the Montmorency diversions. Organized by the host and hostess, these banks more than paid for the luxuries of the table and the upkeep and expenses of the house.

II

Lulled into security by the power of her new protector, all through these pleasant months Catherine continued her friendship with Cristofero Spinola and, as often as she dared, wrote to the Vicomte de Lambertye in London. Mischievously she told him of her association with Talleyrand, unkindly referring to the august Citizen-Minister by a nickname. She called him l'Abbé Piécourt. Piécourt—the limp-foot—was ever at her side, she wrote to Lambertye. He was ready to lay his scepter at her feet. . . . Monsieur de Talleyrand did not know of the undignified nickname she had bestowed on him, but he was quite aware of the secret correspondence with Lambertye. In fact, he encouraged it, for it was by this indirect means that he kept in touch with England, particularly with his old friend Robert Smith, clerk of the Treasury.

The police, meanwhile, had forgotten neither Cristofero Spinola nor Madame Grand. They were still watching, still waiting. Convinced that Spinola was a conspirator, they inferred that the lady was his associate. True, she was the friend of the Minister of Foreign Affairs, but Talleyrand himself was a cunning fox. One never quite knew what tricks he might play. It was wise to watch and wait.

One day, having written her usual letter to Lambertye, Catherine gave it to Spinola to smuggle out of France. He passed it on to a secret courier. But the courier had a friend and the friend stole the letter. When he had read it from end to end he sent it to the Directory, to Minister Laréveillère in fact, who hated Talleyrand as he hated the devil. Though the letter in no way compromised the Minister of Foreign Affairs politically, Laréveillère locked it away carefully among his secret papers. It was a weapon that might prove useful in his dealings with that haughty limp-foot Talleyrand. However, Spinola was immediately arrested. A sentence of expulsion was pronounced on him and he was bundled off to England. Meanwhile, too, the police had visited Madame Grand at Montmorency.

She held her head high when the captain of police showed her his warrant for arrest. "On what charge, I pray you?" she demanded imperiously, looking him full in the face.

"Of trafficking with the enemies of the Republic," he replied.

"You are insane, Captain. I command you to order your men to leave my house immediately." But her throat felt dry as she uttered these words, and her head was reeling.

"Come, *citoyenne*. Not so much fuss. We have letters—"

"Written by whom?" she cried sharply.

"By *Citoyenne* Grand to the Vicomte de Lambertye, enemy of France," came the short reply.

"It is false. I can explain all," she protested.

"No doubt. And you will have an opportunity to explain. But not here. Come, *citoyenne*."

She tried to speak but no words came. An awful nausea of fear swept over her. She put out her hand to steady herself and the next instant collapsed in a heap on the floor. Of what happened after this she had but a blurred impression. When at last her senses cleared the hideous reality of prison walls encompassed her. She sat huddled in misery, past all thought and only semiconscious through fear. For two nights she did not sleep.

But neither did Monsieur de Talleyrand. On the very night of her arrest he wrote to Barras.

CITIZEN DIRECTOR,

Madame Grand has just been arrested as a conspirator. She is the person in all Europe the furthest from and the least capable of embarking on an affair of this kind. She is a very lovely Indian, very indolent and the idlest woman I have ever met. I beg your influence on her behalf, for I am sure not even a shadow of a pretext can be found against her or against putting an end to this affair to which I shall be sorry to see publicity given. I love her and I declare to you, as man to man, that never in her life did she meddle, or has she been capable of meddling, in any business whatever. She is a genuine Indian and you know to what a degree this species of womankind is a stranger to intrigue.

Greetings and attachment,
CH. MAUR. TALLEYRAND.

Thus disdainfully did the Minister of Foreign Affairs, who at this stage imagined himself truly in love for the first time in his life, write of his lady. His nature was a cesspool of hypocrisy and brutal cynicism. These qualities were to him what familiar imps are to a sorcerer. So he could never abstain from ridiculing or expressing contempt even for those most near and dear to him. Still he had written to Barras, written urgently, and anxiously he awaited the result of his plea.

III

Paris seethed with gossip. The Press flaunted the story and though Talleyrand managed to subdue the friendly newspapers, there were others which even he could not reduce to silence. These persisted in their clamor. One went so far as to publish a picture of the august Minister of Foreign Affairs with the portrait of his mistress, in place of the episcopal cross, dangling on his breast, while from his pockets, in a great cascade, tumbled the letters written by Catherine to Lambertye.

Barras, meanwhile, had not neglected Talleyrand's strangely expressed entreaty to come to Catherine's aid. With the best of intentions and the friendliest feelings toward the Minister of Foreign Affairs, he acted promptly and brought the matter before a small body of the Directorate. Under the impression that the case could be treated with the kind of contemptuous indifference with which Talleyrand had imbued it, he asked quite simply that Catherine be set at liberty. His demand raised a hornets' nest and was met by a passionate outburst from his colleagues.

There were gathered together at this impromptu meeting which Barras summarily convened, some of the most violent of Talleyrand's opponents in the Directory—Reubell, Laréveillère, and Merlin. All three of them were burning to oust the Minister of Foreign Affairs from his office. Reubell opened the attack, speaking in the name of virtue and morality.

"Citizens and colleagues," he began, in a white heat of passion, "when the National Convention struck from the list of *émigrés* the name of Talleyrand, he asserted that he had spent the days of his exile from France in the United States and had enjoyed the friendship of the illustrious chiefs of the American republic. Well then, I now ask if the morals practiced by him in this country are those he received an example of at the hands of the Washingtons and Jeffersons. . . . What does he take us for that he should dare to come and make a display of his cynicism? . . . This wretched unfrocked, or rather still frocked priest, who, not content with being the vilest of libertines, cannot gratify his desires in France—which certainly is not lacking in strumpets—must needs go and seek one in England, and one of those to boot whom Englishmen import from India, just as they import wines from Oporto, which would not be strong enough were they not subjected to several sea voyages. Talleyrand would not enjoy life unless spiced with a scandal proclaimed from the housetops. . . . I demand that the appointment of this impudent priest be cancelled."

Merlin of the protruding teeth said: "My dear colleagues, I fail to discover any excuse for Talleyrand from the moral point of view, and were it possible to find an excuse for him, looking at him as a private individual, it might perhaps result in aggravating his case as a political person. For after all, as said by our colleague, women are not scarce in France, supposing that our passions called for them. There are so many of them, all lovely, kind and excellent." He paused for an instant, smirking at his colleagues, as if subtly petitioning for forbearance in trifling personal sins which he would rather have enjoyed admitting.

Reubell, quick to interpret that half-supplicating, affected smile, snapped out sharply: "But you are, like ourselves, a married man, hence you do not require being forgiven mistresses you do not have. If, however, you wish to appear a Céladon in order to acquire rights to indulge, tell us what there is to be told. Let us hear all about your ladykilling exploits."

Merlin's lips drew back in a thin malicious snarl. "All that I can say about myself," he declared sourly, "is that when I have the pleasure of possessing a woman, not only do I not boast of the fact, but I do not admit it; much less do I name the lady. . . . Since, then, we all agree that France is not lacking in lovely, accommodating women, why, if one desires the need of them, should one go and seek them in British India?

"There is in this something, I must confess, which seems to me to leave the private domain and belong altogether to that of politics. Who will guarantee us that this alleged gallant liaison of Talleyrand with this loved woman is not a political liaison, of which love is only the official screen? Who is there, in short, to guarantee that Madame Grand, owing to her disrepute, was not for that very reason looked upon as the woman who could best don the appearance of a gallant rôle intended to conceal the rôle of political falseness?

"Lastly, is not Talleyrand, against whom so many patriots have brought the charge, a man sold to England, an actual agent of England, of whom Madame Grand is only the intermediary packet boat?

"I therefore ask that, instead of restoring liberty to the woman Grand, the Minister of Police be instructed to question her himself, very closely. This affair should be proved to the quick. We cannot close our eyes to what Talleyrand really is. In order to catch Talleyrand in *flagrante delicto,* we must, however, appear to look upon the matter as one of slight importance, so that he may be less on his guard; nay, we must go so far as to receive him kindly when he comes before the Directorate on ministerial business. If, as I hope, we succeed in unearthing the plot, we will make a striking example of him, and after dismissing him we will send him for trial before a military commission. Madame Grand naturally falls under the cognisance of such a tribunal since she is an émigrée who has returned to France."

For some time during Merlin's long speech, François de Neufchâteau had shifted uneasily in his chair. Remembering his own ever-recurring peccadilloes he felt hot and uncomfortable. Now suddenly he jumped to his feet. "The Directory has undoubtedly a right to keep an eye on the political conduct of its agents," he thundered, "but it has no right to meddle with their private life. That is a sanctuary."

Reubell looked at him curiously. So the young man's conscience was pricking him. A fine way to plead one's own case. De Neufchâteau was a fool. A great fool. . . . But before he could speak, the virtuous, narrow-minded Laréveillère jumped up and held the floor, his heart afire with hatred against Talleyrand.

"Citizen colleagues," he shouted, "Talleyrand is doing in this instance only what he has done all his life: he screens his intrigues with his licentiousness, or his licentiousness with his intrigues. It all amounts to the same thing. His double-faced character is, as a matter of course, open to suspicion in regard to all he does and in connection with everything." Laréveillère went on and on in this vein, lashing himself into so great a fury that his eyes bulged and his body trembled. With equal violence he thundered against Talleyrand's libertinism and the Church of Rome.

At last Barras brought him to silence. "It seems to me," said Barras, "that we are all agreed at least upon one thing, to throw light upon this affair, in order to be able better to judge of it. Hence the first thing to be done is to refer it to the Minister of Police."

After some debate this motion was carried.

Three days later, in spite of the denunciations and vituperative explosions of Merlin, Laréveillère, and Reubell, the prison gates were opened for Catherine Grand. All her private papers which had been confiscated were handed back to her. She returned to Montmorency. Such was the power and genius of Talleyrand.

For a little while longer the scandal steamed and bubbled. Then gradually it lessened. Barras, believing "that it was still a far cry from a greatly relaxed morality in private life to political treachery," was firmly of the opinion that Talleyrand was incapable of treason. But with a section of the Directorate the Minister of Foreign Affairs was in worse repute than ever.

IV

Once again surrounded by the liberty of Montmorency, Catherine was neither happy nor at peace. Close about her pressed the horrors of the prison from which she had so recently escaped. Her nights were hideous with dreams. The shadow of anxiety stalked her by day. She was often in tears. At every unfamiliar sound she was filled with apprehension.

"*Mon ami*, I shall die," she declared repeatedly to Talleyrand. "I cannot live in this uncertainty. What am I to do? Where am I to go? I pray to *le bon Dieu*, but He does not seem to hear me." Then she wept like a child, burying her face in her hands.

Talleyrand always listened to her quietly, his lazy glance now resting on her hair, now on her white throat. But when she began to sob, he soothed her grief with ardent promises and protestations. He could be very gentle if he chose. . . .

Catherine's belief in Talleyrand's power intoxicated her senses. She no longer thought of him mischievously and rather unkindly as l'Abbé Piécourt. She could no longer look at him dispassionately. She felt a peculiar reverence for him which, at first influenced by her head, now completely dominated her heart. He stood before her strangely transformed by her gratitude. For the first time in her life she began to regret her past. She longed to cut herself off from it forever. She wanted to begin a new life, a life linked with the fortunes and fate of Charles Maurice de Talleyrand, once the Bishop of Autun.

But outweighing all other things in time and importance was the dire problem of preventing a repetition of that dreadful prison episode. Eagerly, and knowing that he would find a solution, she turned to Talleyrand for help. He was quick to evolve a scheme. There was only one way of setting about the business. She must without delay seek the favors of the Directory.

He himself drew up and endorsed the petition which she submitted. In it the fact that she had been born in a Danish colony in India of French parents was carefully pointed out. Furthermore, the document asserted that though she had married an English official, the unhappiness which he had caused her had been so great that, through him, she had lost all her affection for England. Under the circumstances, therefore, it was indeed a tragedy that she should have been suspected of acting as an agent of that country. Her greatest desire in life was to sever her connection with Great Britain finally and forever by divorcing a husband whom she had not heard from in five long years. Most humbly she beseeched the Directorate to consider her petition and to grant her request for divorce, for by this means only would she be able to break with the past completely. . . .

At this time, in distant India, George François Grand was seriously beginning to contemplate a visit to England. Fate had been meting out harsh treatment to him recently, and, though he looked prosperous, for he had grown enormously fat, he was very much down on his luck.

When he had first left Calcutta for Patna, fortune had favored him liberally. Within a comparatively short time he had risen from the position of commerical assistant of the factory to that of Governor of the Provinces of Tirhoot and Hajeepore. At Tirhoot he had acquired large private indigo interests and had grown very prosperous. But alas, on the arrival of Lord Cornwallis in India, he was summarily dismissed from office by "one stroke of his lordship's pen" and, in addition, was forced to give up his indigo concerns. When, turning rancorous, he had opposed law and authority with contempt—he had become excessively quarrelsome and more self-important than ever before—he was charged with his misdemeanors. "Possibly there might have been errors of form in my administration," he admitted in writing years later, "but I dare my worst enemy to come forward with any accusation involving or bordering on criminality."

Finding it impossible to gain redress for his grievances in India, he began a wordy and lengthy correspondence with the Court of Directors in England. But his repeated appeals were of no avail. For a time Grand went from pillar to post in an attempt to earn a livelihood. At one period he was on the jury of Calcutta; at another he acted as a commissioner for the scheme of a lottery; still later he was appointed to the position of officer in charge of dispatching the mail boat for Europe at Diamond Harbour. At last he began seriously planning a voyage to London to seek redress for his grievances personally from the Court of Directors of the East India Company.

It was at this time that Catherine sent her petition for divorce to the Directory. She had little difficulty in getting her plea conceded, since the revolutionary law granted dissolution of marriage contracts on the flimsiest pretexts. So, though she was a Catholic united in matrimony to George François Grand according to both the Catholic and Protestant rites, her marriage to him was annulled on April 7, 1798, in the Town Hall of the Second Arrondissement of Paris. From now on she no longer merely "frequented" the Hôtel Gallifet. She went to live there permanently and openly as Talleyrand's mistress. During these halcyon days Talleyrand was as deeply in love with her as it was possible for him to be with any human being except himself, and she, fortified with happiness, was determined to follow him and his fortunes wherever they might lead.

Chapter Four

I

On February 19, 1800, Napoleon Bonaparte, who in less than a decade had made himself the virtual master of France, took up residence at the Tuileries as First Consul. "Come, little Creole," he said to Josephine that night in the bedchamber of the kings of France. "Come. Get into the bed of your masters."

The magical career of this great little vulgar man of low stature had begun during the Revolution when, as the friend of that "sea-green incorruptible" Robespierre, he had won glory for himself by recapturing Toulon from the English. In those days he was a Jacobin. When Robespierre fell from power and shared the fate of his thousands of victims, Bonaparte too was arrested. The splendid military services which he had rendered to France, however, saved him from the guillotine, and he lived to become the protégé of Barras and Carnot. For them, with a "whiff of grapeshot," he not only defeated the October Revolution of 1795, but through its defeat ended the French Revolution completely so that it "became a thing that was." Then he began to dream. His was a strange, fascinating dream of power. No one knew of the visions that lay in his mind.

Barras and Carnot put him in command of the Army of Italy, but even before Campo Formio he wrote these burning words: "Do you think I triumph in Italy for the glory of the lawyers of the Directory, a Carnot or a Barras? Do you suppose I mean to found a Republic? What an idea! A Republic of thirty million people! With our morals, our vices! How is such a thing possible? The nation wants a chief, a chief covered with glory. . . ."

The lawyers of the Directory had seen in Bonaparte only a

military genius. But shrewder and more farsighted, Talleyrand saw deeper. From the very moment that he set foot in Paris again, he kept his eye on the Corsican. He realized from the start that Bonaparte was the real, the only "strong man" in the great political drama of France. Cunningly and systematically, therefore, he applied himself to win the confidence and friendship of the young Corsican general. And he succeeded as he always succeeded in everything on which he set his mind.

With Talleyrand's flattering tributes ringing in his ears Bonaparte started on his Egyptian campaign in 1798. Josephine accompanied him to Toulon and from there proceeded to Plombiéres in the hope that, after two years of married life, the waters of this spa would make her conceive. Reubell, too, was at Plombiéres at this time. He was desperately sick. In his infirmity he symbolized the depressed government of which he was a minister. For within recent times the Directory had fallen into grave disorder. Intrigues flourished at home and abroad and conditions in France were steadily growing worse.

His tongue in his cheek, Talleyrand, the father of changes in government, sat waiting for the deluge. With a damp finger he tested the strength of the rising gale and kept his eye on Bonaparte. An election came and he fell from office together with Merlin and Laréveillère. But the fall barely ruffled his calm exterior. His mind was much too busy with future events. When he moved from the Hôtel Gallifet to a small house in a side street, Catherine did not desert him. She went with him to share his semiretirement. At a window on the first floor of this house in the Rue Taitbout she stood beside him listening to the rising wind of discord and dissatisfaction which blew across France. Day by day the storm became more fierce. Now often in the streets cries of "Long live the sans-culottes!" were followed in turn by even louder shouts of "Long live the king!" Like a flimsy house in an earth tremor, the Directory rocked on its foundations. Reubell said that Talleyrand in his semiretirement fell asleep at night reading lampoons about himself. But that was only partly true. For though there were lampoons enough to send him to sleep, actually he slept very little at this period. All day and half the night he was working, warily and silently as was his wont, preparing for that psychological moment when the Corsican would return from Egypt to strike an effective blow in French politics.

At last Bonaparte arrived. He went to live in a house he had bought from the actor Talma in the Rue Chautereine, recently renamed the Rue de la Victoire in his honor. His new home, filled with furniture decorated with symbols of war and victory befitting the conqueror of Arcola and Rivoli, delighted him. But he spent much of his time at Talleyrand's house in the Rue Taitbout. There in the dimly lit study he would sit for hours on end, talking in a low voice of a mysterious project. Sometimes, with Roederer, Sieyès, and Fouché he appeared in the drawing room, where, to deaden the scent of conspiracy, Talleyrand sat playing whist with Catherine Grand and Madame de Cambis.

With the complicated machinations of political intrigue Catherine troubled her head but little. She was aware that the Government of France was tottering precariously and that Bonaparte was waiting to glide into power. But Talleyrand saw to it that she remained but half initiated in the comings and goings at the Rue Taitbout. In his symphony of intrigue she had only one note to play, that of the beautiful and delightful hostess in his drawing room who flattered and charmed his guests with pleasing attentions.

So the weeks passed, till at last, on the night of the 15th Brumaire, the secret plottings, discussions, and preparations came to an end. Everything was in readiness awaiting the zero hour. That arrived three days later at St. Cloud, where the Council of Ancients had summoned the Legislative Assembly. On that day, to the shouts of *À bas les dictateurs,* Bonaparte, and with him Talleyrand, Sieyès, and Fouché, effected a grand coup d'état. The Directory was dissolved. Fascinated by Bonaparte, the nation wholeheartedly approved this violent stroke of state policy and cheered lustily. Everywhere there was hope that order and prosperity would again be restored to France. The five percent *rentes* soared to seventeen. Talleyrand, with his nose for money, speculated and made a fortune. Bonaparte became the First Consul and Fouché "the policeman of the Quai Malaquais." And on the night of February 19th, when Josephine slept at the Tuileries in the bedchamber of the kings of France for the first time, Catherine Grand was back in her old apartments at the Hôtel Gallifet. For Monsieur de Talleyrand was once again Minister of Foreign Affairs.

II

A new France had been born—France of the Consulate, which opened its arms wide to the Royalists who had fled during the Revolution. Catherine's name was struck off the list of émigrés and it was decreed that she was to be known in the future in all official documents as "Catherine Noël Werlée, by marriage Grand, native of Denmark." In addition, all the property that had been confiscated from her house in the Rue Mirabeau in 1792 was returned to her.

Having made his peace with the émigrés, Bonaparte turned his attention to the Church of Rome. Here, too, he deemed it politic to have complete and undisturbed harmony. So Monsignor Spina was invited to come from Rome to act as religious plenipotentiary, and the churches of Paris once again opened their doors for public worship. But there still remained one thorn to be plucked from the rose of ordered relationship, namely, the ban of excommunication which teasingly pricked the august Minister of Foreign Affairs. Not only did Monsieur de Talleyrand desire annulment of this sentence, he had set his heart on complete secularization. Unfortunately, on the latter question His Holiness Pope Pius VII did not see eye to eye with the former Bishop of Autun, and though he withdrew the ban of excommunication he did not find his way clear to restoring his "beloved son, Charles Maurice de Talleyrand" to the laity. In short, after all his scheming, the Minister of Foreign Affairs found himself a priest again and a onetime bishop still bound by the strict vows of celibacy.

III

Josephine was now mistress of the Tuileries, and Catherine Grand was the chatelaine of the Hôtel Gallifet. Since Talleyrand had become the most important man in France after Bonaparte, the Hôtel of External Relations ranked next in consequence to the Tuileries. Indeed, Monsieur de Talleyrand's salon blossomed into the most popular rendezvous in Paris. Some of the finest assemblies since the days of the old regime were held there. It became a sort of melting pot in which the France of Louis XVI simmered amicably with the France of the Consulate. Bonaparte showed himself there occasionally, but Josephine came oftener and stayed longer. Here Sieyès talked with the Chevalier de Coligny; the Duc de Laval brought Madame the Duchess; Madame de Flahaut listened to the malicious wit of Monsieur de Montrond; young Eugéne Beauharnais discussed the war with General Marat; and Admiral Bruix paid compliments to the Duchesse de Fleury. They were all there, all Talleyrand's friends. Only Madame de Staël did not come. A short, formal refusal to dinner had been Talleyrand's dismissal of this woman who had so generously helped him back to power four years earlier.

At these great feasts at the Hôtel Gallifet Catherine Grand was the presiding goddess who played hostess. She was gracious and, if not in wit at least in loveliness, she far outshone the grand ladies who fluttered around the brilliant Minister of Foreign Affairs, surfeiting his little dog Jonquille with sweets for love of him.

These days passed in great happiness for Catherine. Serenely beautiful, she would wander among the guests at the Hôtel Gallifet dispensing hospitality; or calmly, her hands folded in her lap, she would watch Madame Vestris and Mademoiselle Chameroi dance Russian gavottes and listen to the great Garat and Madame Walbonne sing enchantingly for the pleasure of Monsieur de Talleyrand's visitors. She always wore magnificent clothes and jewels; she was present at all the first nights at the Opéra and the Vaudeville; she went walking in the Bois in spring, a tiny sunshade held above her head; she drove along the Champs-Élysées, indolently reclining in her carriage drawn by two huge, spanking bays.

When Talleyrand hired a lovely villa at Neuilly from Delannoy the contractor, she found another reason for happiness. The new villa became dearer to her than the ninety-nine columned Hôtel Gallifet in the Rue du Bac. It was here at Neuilly, after the Peace of Lunéville, that she helped Talleyrand entertain the hereditary Prince of Parma and his wife, who had been newly created king and queen of Etruria. The grand feast which the Minister of Foreign Affairs gave at his summer villa in their honor was a "triumph of genius," a triumph which Catherine shared with Talleyrand, for she was ever at his side dispensing the honors of his house. Never since the days of Marie Antoinette had so magnificent an assembly been seen in France. The fine park of Neuilly was transformed into a semblance of Florence, a fairyland Florence. Even a Pitti Palace gleamed among the trees. Fireworks starred the heavens and peasants danced among the flower beds. Supper that night was served three times in five rooms, and the whole magnificent entertainment came to an end with a brilliant ball which lasted till the morning.

The flower-embowered villa of Neuilly became Catherine's little court. There she reigned in state, receiving and entertaining the famous diplomats, foreigners, politicians, and men of letters who gathered about Bonaparte's illustrious Minister of Foreign Affairs like bees around a jar of honey. The fame of her select suppers spread far and wide. Stories were told of how "the Service was in Grecian style; nymphs with mythological names served the coffee from golden ewers, and perfumes burned in silver chafing dishes," and, like an Eastern princess, Madame Grand was followed wherever she went by a retinue of richly attired Oriental servants.

In short, Catherine Grand was the talk of Paris. Linked with Talleyrand, she had become one of the most prominent women in France under the Consulate.

IV

At this time Catherine was in the prime of that beauty which, even more than chance, had raised her to the position she held in the household of the Minister of Foreign Affairs. For Talleyrand's passion for her was more than three-quarters sensual. He willingly forgave her mental and spiritual shortcomings because of the indescribable pleasure she gave to his senses. Physically he found her perfect.

"Tell me," said Montrond to Talleyrand one day, "what possible attraction can you find in the conversation of this woman with the pretty face?"

Talleyrand shrugged his shoulders. "What would you have me say?" he declared. "It is a recreation for me. She is a pleasing companion and as beautiful as a goddess. Besides, she refreshes me after Madame de Staël."

Catherine's nature was, indeed, a great contrast to the fiery temperament and genius of Necker's daughter. She was simple and good-humored. In spite of her physical loveliness she was not glaringly vain. She enjoyed flattery and compliments rather as a child enjoys its toys. At this period of her life she was still too completely artless and unaffected to give herself airs. That was to come later caused rather by the people around her than the exalted position she attained.

Not only did she at this time possess a childlike grace and carriage, she also had a pleasing manner of speech and delightfully gay and tender ways. She was always serene. In truth, she was too indolent to fly into furies. This trait in her nature particularly pleased the easygoing Talleyrand, who hated scenes above all things. Though he gave her provocation enough since he infrequently took pains to hide his infidelity to her, she seldom indulged in tears of jealousy and never in the fits of hysteria verging on convulsions he had become familiar with in his association with Madame de Staël.

In these stirring days of the Consulate he had need of a restful companion, such a one as Catherine who, by her good nature, her loyalty, and her abysmal indolence, satisfied him completely. For the time being he was perfectly content with her for, as he told a boon companion: "She has not sense enough to indulge in political intrigue and grace and beauty enough to do the honors of my house."

So admirable was Catherine's understanding of *l'art de tenir son salon,* and so invaluable at this particular period was this talent of hers to Talleyrand, that he considered it infinitely more important than the bons mots of the most brilliant women of France. So he chose her, instead of one of the grand ladies of social standing, to play Egeria at his receptions. To all who frequented his salon she showed herself gracious and charming. What did it matter under the circumstances, said Talleyrand, if her knowledge and interests were limited? And if her conversation was not starred with wit and brilliance—indeed, she was often guilty of errors in speech because of her unaffected simplicity and naïve manner of expression—she never displeased him by committing social blunders.

In Paris Catherine's beauty provoked one opinion only—that of unequivocal admiration. With regard to her mental faculties, however, there were two opinions. The affected wits led by Montrond, and those who were jealous of her position in Talleyrand's house, declared that whenever she opened her mouth something foolish came out of it. On the other hand, those who knew her really well considered her lovable and neither ignorant nor stupid. Her conversation, they admitted, was not distinguished by wit but neither was it the silly conversation of a fool.

Talleyrand, wilier than the wiliest, successfully turned the indirect shafts of ridicule away from himself by joining in the laughter of the scoffers, and himself frequently spoke mockingly of his mistress's foolishness and lack of understanding. "What would you have, she has as much sense as a rose," he would say, borrowing a phrase from Chamfort. Thus, slyly fostered by him, Catherine's stupidity became proverbial. It was almost as fashionable at one time to quote her "silly sayings" as to collect the bons mots of the Minister of Foreign Affairs. Society was prodigiously amused and asked for more, and to meet the demand Montrond and his circle of malicious wits twisted her simplest remarks into the grossest imbecilities. Many a stupid "saying" was attributed to her which had never passed her lips, most famous of all being the celebrated phrase *Je suis d'Inde* which, as the answer to a question put to her about her nationality, was alleged to have been uttered by her as *Je suis dinde*—"*dinde*" being used in the same sense as "goose."

Another story of Catherine's foolishness which had a great vogue in Paris was connected with Denon, the Egyptologist. When he arrived in Paris soon after the return of the army from Egypt, Talleyrand invited him to dinner, instructing Catherine as to her behavior toward the great savant in the following manner: "He is a very charming man, an author, and authors, you know, like to be questioned about their work. So I shall give you an account of his voyages and you must read it in order to discuss it with him."

The story went on to tell how Talleyrand did indeed send a book to Catherine's apartment, but in error, instead of Denon's voyages, sent Defoe's *Robinson Crusoe*.

On the night of the dinner Denon was given the place of honor next to Madame Grand. "Ah, monsieur," she said turning to him eagerly, "I cannot express all the pleasure I found in reading your strange adventures."

"Madame, you are too kind," he answered.

"No, I assure you," she declared. "But how miserable you must have felt all alone on that desert island. I was specially interested in that."

Denon stared at her, puzzled. "I think, madame—" he began.

But she interrupted with a smile, "You must have looked very funny in your pointed hat."

"Truly, madame, I—I don't understand—" Denon muttered in frantic bewilderment.

"Oh, but I *do* understand, all your trials and tribulations!" she answered in a voice trembling with sympathy. "How you must have suffered!"

"Indeed, madame, I—I don't know what—I can't—" he stammered in confusion.

"It must have been dreadful," she continued kindly. "How pleased you must have been the day you found Friday."

This story went the round of Paris society, indeed of all Europe. Yet years later when Talleyrand was questioned as to its authenticity, he replied: "It did not actually happen. The circumstance did not really occur as it has been represented, for I was there to prevent it. However, it was guessed at and that was enough for the blunder to be ascribed to her without compunction."

Denon, in fact, became very kindly disposed to Catherine and out of friendship presented her with a charming little ape which she called Simia. Simia was an amusing creature, full of pranks and cunning ways, and at the Hôtel of External Relations she soon rivaled the little dog Jonquille in popularity. Simia's amazing proficiency at sealing letters delighted even Monsieur de Talleyrand, with whom she became a prime favorite, and she spent many hours of the day gamboling about in his study. But it was Josephine Bonaparte who truly doted on the little ape. At last, after much persuasion, Catherine parted with her pet and Simia went to live at Malmaison as a token of Catherine's affectionate friendship for the wife of the First Consul of France.

But to return to the recital of Catherine Grand's alleged stupidities. If a statement is made often and loudly enough, the world begins to believe it. So it was that soon Paris was firmly persuaded that, being beautiful, it was quite natural that Catherine should be silly. She herself added fuel to this fire by often declaring naïvely that she was indeed a *belle-bête*. If she had been a great lady her innocently unaffected remark would, without doubt, have been considered extremely witty. Since, however, she was no *grande dame* it was looked upon as further proof of her stupidity.

But she was not the *belle-bête* she professed to be. Would Talleyrand have chosen her to play hostess in his salon if she had been completely devoid of sense? If she did not always behave with as much dignity as she might have done, that, for him, was part of her childlike charm. In reality she possessed a fund of common sense, and she was in no way inferior to "ordinary persons against whom no one ever thinks of bringing a charge of unusual stupidity." But fashionable society, particularly the wits and the women friends of the Minister of Foreign Affairs, continued to hold her up to ridicule. They resented her position and mocked her because she lacked the traditions of Talleyrand's world. For Catherine, despite her social ornamentation and veneer, remained in her innermost self the daughter of a minor official of Chandernagore who had been born with a golden spoon in her mouth.

Chapter Five

I

Early in the year 1802 all Europe went into wild rejoicing at the signing of a treaty at Amiens which brought a temporary respite from the long years of war between France, Spain and the Batavian Republics on the one side, and England on the other. Paris, aflutter with flags by day and a fairyland of lights by night, was invaded by a host of famous foreigners anxious to enjoy its gaieties and pleasures and the splendid fetes and receptions given by the First Consul at the Tuileries.

Talleyrand, who had prepared the terms of the treaty, shared almost equally with Bonaparte in the honors of the peace, and all Europe paid him court with respect and awe. His opinions were quoted everywhere. Visitors carefully jotted down his sparkling jests and witty sayings in their notebooks and poets inscribed their verses to him. Those who sought his society by frequenting the receptions at the Hôtel Gallifet, or by getting themselves invited to the *petits soupers* and *soirées* at the Villa Neuilly had perforce to accept the presence of Catherine Grand, for at all Monsieur de Talleyrand's entertainments she was the presiding queen.

Many a famous visitor was somewhat surprised to find so great a man as the Minister of Foreign Affairs raising into prominence a mistress who had at one time been a woman of the town. They considered it a weakness. However, since she was not only beautiful to look at but certainly did the honors of his table and salon with extraordinary graciousness, the majority felt that recognition of her position in his household was a small price to pay for the society of the wittiest of conversationalists, the greatest man in France after Bonaparte.

186

Unfortunately, on this matter the ambassadresses from foreign courts thought otherwise. Even the glamor of Monsieur de Talleyrand could not console them for the fact that the woman who dispensed the hospitality of his house had been a courtesan of Paris. Point-blank, therefore, they refused to be received at the Hôtel Gallifet by Madame Grand. Their dissatisfaction spread like wildfire and, with the deliberate intention of doing harm to Talleyrand's prestige, Fouché brought the scandal to the ears of the First Consul. Fuming with anger, Bonaparte, who was fully determined to have his court steeped in at least outward respectability, sent for his Minister of Foreign Affairs. Once and for all he would put an end to this public scandal.

The First Consul began the stormy interview with a suggestion that Talleyrand should resume the episcopal robes or, better still, allow himself to be invested with the purple apparel of a cardinal. Talleyrand's reply, though icily courteous, was obstinately and unyieldingly in the negative. He did not consider himself fit for the priesthood, he maintained, and nothing whatsoever would induce him to reenter the order. Very well then, declared Bonaparte, that ended the matter. His Minister of Foreign Affairs might refuse to be made a cardinal, but with regard to Catherine Grand he would have to submit to convention and decency by dismissing her instantly from his house. At all costs, said the First Consul, he was determined to stamp the new Court of France with the seal of moral rectitude.

II

Selfish, unprincipled, and shameless, it did not take Talleyrand long to make up his mind how he would act toward Catherine. Audaciously dissolute and with neither pity nor decency in his heart, he prepared to expel from his house the woman who had given him her fidelity and affection and four years of her life. Enough was enough. The woman had become a habit with him and it was high time that the habit was broken. Yet, because he remembered that he had found her very sweet and that her beauty and even temper, her childlike simplicity and indolence had once suited his easygoing nature, he covered the pill of dismissal thickly with the sugar of flattery and cajolement.

But Catherine was quick to taste its bitterness. It was unthinkable and impossible for her, at this stage of her life, to be forced back into the precarious existence of a woman of the town. How could she let him break with her? What was to become of her if he banished her from his house? In the solitude of her apartment she abandoned herself to her perplexity and grief. Before her tear-dimmed eyes she saw all the luxuries, triumphs, and joys that had become the mainspring of her existence, and that Talleyrand alone could give her, crumbling into dust. . . .

At this critical point in her life when her anxieties became more than she could bear, ghosts of her Calcutta youth that she thought long since laid, suddenly appeared to add to her unhappiness. Unexpectedly and almost simultaneously Sir Elijah and Lady Impey, Philip Francis, and George François Grand arrived in Paris.

To get Francis out of the way was a comparatively easy matter. Catherine wrote him a little note. She told him of the position in which she was placed, vaguely hinted at the possibility of marriage with the Minister of Foreign Affairs, and regretted that in the circumstances it was impossible for her to receive him, since she was most anxious not to offend Monsieur de Talleyrand.

Francis replied in the most charming and courteous manner, declaring that "it was his pleasure to hear of any circumstance that would attribute to that happiness which she so well deserved and he so much desired to hear her possess, that her least wishes would always be law to him and that he would not now or ever intrude upon her presence; except in case of any change of situation she would accept his services, when she would find his esteem and regard unaltered." Furthermore, aware that his presence in Paris might prove an embarrassment to her at this moment in her life, he cut his visit short and returned to England.

In farewell Catherine sent him "a few elegant books" with the assurance that she would never forget him.

It was not so easy to get rid of Grand. Though she used a great deal of gentle persuasion, employing the wily Sir Elijah Impey who frequented the villa at Neuilly as intermediary, she failed to get Grand to pack his bags as gallantly as Philip Francis had done. Having established himself comfortably at the Hôtel du Cercle in the Rue de Richelieu, he declared that he had come to Paris with the express purpose of visiting its impressive monuments and that as yet he was far from surfeited. Actually, however, the object of his visit was mainly that of securing a lucrative post through Catherine's influence with Monsieur de Talleyrand. Until he had got what he had come for, he refused to budge.

Realizing that in his present mood the former Bishop of Autun would be only too willing to return a long-lost wife to George François Grand, Catherine did her best to keep her divorced husband's presence in Paris from Talleyrand's knowledge, at least until she had made her final effort to secure her position in the household of the Minister of Foreign Affairs. This last effort was a visit to the First Consul's wife at Malmaison.

Josephine had been her good friend for many years; they visited each other regularly; and it was to Josephine that she had given her much-loved ape, Simia, as a token of deep affection. Into her friend's sympathetic ear Catherine, on this visit, poured her sorrow, imploring Josephine to plead her cause with the First Consul. The mistress of Malmaison rose nobly to the occasion. She ascended to Bonaparte's cabinet by a private staircase and in a comparatively short time persuaded him of the urgency of the case. She induced him to return with her to her apartments to hear Madame Grand's sad plea from her own lips. Upon the entrance of the First Consul, Catherine fell on her knees before him in a flood of tears. A melancholy, meditative expression on his face, he stood quite still for a moment staring down at her trembling form. Then: "Well, madame?" he demanded impatiently.

In silence she raised her face to his stern gaze. "H'm!" muttered Bonaparte. "Rouge and tears—these two things are very becoming to a woman. . . . But come, madame. Speak."

His gray-blue eyes never left her face for an instant while he listened to her story and her passionate entreaties. Minute by minute his grim austerity softened. More eloquently than her entreaties and her tears her beauty that day cajoled him.

"Well, well, I see only one way out of this," exclaimed a curiously mild Bonaparte, at last. "Let Talleyrand marry you and all will be arranged. But you must either bear his name or leave his house." With these words he dismissed Catherine from his presence.

Hardly had she gone when he sent for Talleyrand. With calm deliberation he repeated his ultimatum. There was no time to lose, he declared. He would give his Minister of Foreign Affairs twenty-four hours to make up his mind. To Talleyrand's argument that marriage for a bishop, even a former one, was unthinkable and that it would create an even greater scandal than the defamatory gossip which had resulted from his concubinage, Bonaparte answered dryly: "Monsieur de Talleyrand, the Court of the Vatican can do anything." Since he could not make him a cardinal he was determined to make a husband of Talleyrand. And much that he did was for Catherine's sake. Hers was the victory, for his cold stern heart had softened with sympathy under the spell of her beauty.

Bonaparte's ultimatum to his Minister of Foreign Affairs, an ultimatum which would expire in twenty-four hours' time, was almost as good as if it were written in black and white. Talleyrand returned to the Hôtel Gallifet much troubled by the promptness of the decision required of him.

III

Catherine spent the hours after her return from Malmaison in the hands of her hairdresser and her maids. Carefully she chose the jewels and the gown she would wear, a gown of rich white satin and diamonds to set off the whiteness of her skin. She had never looked more beautiful nor more alluring than she did this night which she knew would see either her triumph or her downfall. Small wonder that she felt distressingly restless. Like a caged panther she paced up and down her boudoir when her toilette was completed. Nervously she twisted her handkerchief, ever and again raising it to dry the tears that she could not control. There came a knock at her door.

"Madame, Monsieur de Saint-James desires to pay you his respects," said her maid.

De Saint-James? Yes, yes, she would see him. He was a good, dear, kindly creature. It would relieve the agony of her mind to talk to him. . . . She told him the story of her fears and anxiety. Then suddenly she looked at him beseechingly. "My friend, my good friend," she cried, clasping his hands, "you can help me. Indeed, you can. Listen. Monsieur de Talleyrand has returned from Malmaison. I know, for I asked the *valet de chambre*. He is in his study. Go to him, my kind friend. Speak to him on my behalf, appease him, implore him not to send me away."

De Saint-James kissed her fingertips. "I am at your service, madame. Always at your service," he said. The next moment he was gone. But in less than a quarter of an hour he was back again, looking sheepish and extraordinarily crestfallen. He could not meet her eyes.

"What is the matter?" she cried, rushing toward him. "What did he say? Monsieur, tell me, I pray you. Tell me."

"He will not hear me, madame. Nor you either. He says—"

"Yes, yes," she prompted impatiently.

"He says—enough is enough, and that he has made up his mind. I—I think, madame," stammered the unfortunate De Saint-James, "I think it would be best to abandon the attempt."

She drew away from him as if he were an adder. Contempt and anger burned in her ,eyes. "Abandon!" she cried hotly. "Abandon! If he thinks that he is quit of me so easily, he is mistaken. Do you hear? Mistaken! I shall get that Piécourt made a foot shorter if he is not careful. And as for you, you poor foolish creature, just you watch and see how a woman can deal with your miserable, imbecile sex."

Scornfully she gazed at the amazed and silenced De Saint-James and then, her head high, she turned and walked haughtily to the door that led from her boudoir into the apartments of Monsieur de Talleyrand. With a quick movement she turned the handle. But the door was locked. Monsieur de Talleyrand had thought of that little trick the moment De Saint-James left his presence.

For an instant, confused and surprised, she stood still, fighting back her tears. Then she called loudly for a footman. "Open that door," she commanded when the man appeared, and while he pushed and pulled and rattled the handle she stood watching in angry silence, impatiently tapping her foot. Suddenly a triumphant smile lit up her face. She crossed to her desk, opened a drawer, and drew out a small, recently painted and as yet unframed portrait of Talleyrand. Attaching it to a thin golden chain, she hung it about her neck. At this moment the footman forced the door open.

"You will soon hear from me," she said to De Saint-James as she passed him on her way to the apartments of the Minister of Foreign Affairs.

The great salon was already crowded with guests when Catherine entered, for Talleyrand was giving a dinner to foreign ambassadors and diplomats that night. The moment she appeared every eye in the room was fixed on the portrait that dangled so conspicuously on her breast. Impishly delighted, she paid no attention to the inquisitive glances and accepted the banal compliments meted out to her with a meek and innocent air. Only when the greetings and formal expressions of respect were over did she turn to the company with an enchanting smile.

"I see that you have all noticed the picture," she exclaimed. "Is it not a most excellent likeness? And will you congratulate me, for it is a wedding present from that man!" With the most exquisitely audacious gesture she pointed her finger at Talleyrand.

In a dream Talleyrand listened to the congratulations that were addressed first to Catherine and then to him. For the first time in his life he was too confounded to speak. He opened his mouth and then shut it again. He kept wiping the beads of perspiration that broke out on his forehead. Paris said she was a fool, he mused. Madame Grand a fool! She was as clever as the devil! She had led him into as neat an ambuscade as ever woman had devised for man. . . . This was a triumph for Catherine. He was caught in a net. There was no way out for him. How could he deny her announcement here, before the greatest diplomats and ambassadors of Europe? Why, he would become the laughing-stock of every court, every country—the mock of the world; Talleyrand, the cleverest statesman in Europe, outwitted by the cunning of a woman!

Calm and very pale, he watched her in wonderment. Mistress of the situation, she was all smiles, bubbling over with happiness. And in his heart, strangely, the embers of his old passion glowed with sudden warmth. She was the sort of woman a man does not marry—certainly not such a man as he—but how tantalizingly lovely she was! He had never realized that "the power of habit" would influence him so strongly. . . .

Twenty-four hours later he yielded to Bonaparte and Catherine—influenced, some said, by "the remains of love and also perhaps by the fear of irritating a woman whom it is impossible to suppose he had not admitted to his confidence."

IV

Paris clanged with rumors about the marriage. Was it possible, everyone asked, that Talleyrand should have so little respect for public opinion? Why, the man was still a priest, a former bishop, who had never been dispensed from his vows of celibacy! The woman—well, the woman was no better than she should be, a courtesan, a person of the town! The whole thing was impossible, a whim, a piece of bravado on Talleyrand's part.

To all this chatter and conjecture Talleyrand said not one word. Quietly, with the First Consul's help, he set about procuring from Rome that which he most desired, the legalization of his admittance to lay society. At last Pope Pius VII issued a special *Brève* secularizing his "beloved son Charles Maurice de Talleyrand."

"Opening our benevolent heart on your behalf," ran the Brief, "we grant you the right to wear secular habit and to manage all civil affairs." But, alas, by not so much as a word did the document grant the Minister of Foreign Affairs permission to marry! Bonaparte, however, fully determined to set the yoke of matrimony on Talleyrand's shoulders once and for all, interpreted the Brief in his own way. Cleverly he convinced the public that not only was Talleyrand secularized, but also that he had been granted the right of a layman to contract marriage. And while the Pope and the Nuncios in Rome were still dazed with astonishment and dismay at the First Consul's artifice, Madame Grand married her Minister of Foreign Affairs in Paris.

Because of his equivocal position, Talleyrand arranged that the ceremony should take place with the minimum of publicity. On September 9, 1802, before a few friends at Neuilly, the marriage contract between Catherine Noël Werlée and Charles Maurice de Talleyrand was drawn up by two notaries. In the contract the goods belonging to the bride were enumerated—her clothes, linen, lace, jewels, furniture, diamonds, to the value of 300,000 francs; securities and stocks in a bank in Hamburg; a house in the Rue d'Anjou-Saint-Honoré; and an estate called Pont-de-Sains which had originally belonged to the Duc d'Orléans. Bonaparte, Josephine, Talleyrand's two brothers, Archambault and Boson de Périgord, Secretary of State Maret and the two notaries, Lecerf and Fleury, signed the contract.

The following day, the marriage was celebrated at the *Mairie* of the Tenth Arrondissement of Paris. Talleyrand and Catherine arrived with their witnesses—Roederer, President of the section of the Interior of the Council of State, and Vice Admiral Bruix for the bridegroom, and Radyx Sainte-Foy and General-in-Chief

Beuronville, Envoy Extraordinary and Minister Plenipotentiary of the Republic to the Court of Russia, for the bride. When Talleyrand and his wife had signed the register, the Prince of Nassau-Siegen, "grandee of Spain of the first class, Lieutenant General in the service of His Catholic Majesty, and Admiral in the service of the Empress of Russia," added his name as a token of his friendship. To this civil marriage the curé of the little village of Épinay, situated in the district of which Pierrefitte was the chief town, secretly gave his blessing next day.

Such was the religious ceremony celebrating the marriage of Charles Maurice de Talleyrand, formerly Bishop of Autun, and Catherine Noël, daughter of Pierre Werlée, once Capitaine du Port of Chandernagore in India.

V

Now Madame de Talleyrand once again turned her attention to George François Grand. During the anxious days before her marriage to the Minister of Foreign Affairs, the guest at that hostel "for the accommodation alone of male strangers" (the Hôtel du Cercle in the Rue de Richelieu), had been a source of great anxiety to her. For a few short weeks, with the help of Sir Elijah Impey, she had managed to keep her former husband—from whom she was separated by a divorce the Church of Rome did not recognize and which he could have disavowed—well out of the limelight. But the effort had cost her a considerable amount of money in the form of a liberal pension offered through the negotiations of the Chief of Justice and accepted by Grand.

Unfortunately a person of Grand's caliber could not long be kept in the dark and when his presence in Paris became known, rumor and the pamphleteers got busy with ridicule and malicious gossip. This was irksome for Talleyrand when it got to his ears. He had promised to marry Madame Grand, but he was in no mood to be laughed at and mocked by society. He found George Grand's presence in Paris not only indiscreet but most offensive. Without delay, therefore, he set about the business of ridding the French capital of the ridiculous Anglo-Swiss. In his name he made Catherine write a letter to M. Van der Goes, Minister of Foreign Affairs to the Republic of Batavia, begging him to find a post for Grand in some distant Dutch colony.

Van der Goes proved himself a kind and obliging friend to both Madame Grand and Monsieur de Talleyrand, for he replied immediately, offering Grand the post of Councillor to the Regency at the Cape of Good Hope at a salary of 2,000 florins per annum. Declaring himself well satisfied with the post, Grand departed for Holland, and Monsieur de Talleyrand and Madame Grand, breathing sighs of relief, were married.

Their elation, however, was short-lived for, very soon after their marriage, they discovered to their horror that the miserable Grand, thirsting for the joys of life, had merely deserted the pleasures of Paris for the delights of Amsterdam. Most galling of all, he seemed to have taken root there. Talleyrand again made Catherine write to Van der Goes.

"Sir, I must no longer delay in thanking you for your kindness and for all you have done for M. Grand, at my request," she began her letter. "The eagerness and graciousness which you have shown proves to me that one does not count upon your friendship in vain, and encourages me to ask another favor of you: it is that you will enjoin M. Grand to embark without delay, for it is inconvenient that he should prolong his stay in Amsterdam, where he has now been for a month very much in the way. . . ." She signed this letter "Talleyrand-Périgord, *née* Werlée." She was very proud of her new name. Indeed, when writing another letter to M. Van der Goes just twelve days after her marriage, she had added the following postscript to her letter: "You will see, sir, by the name which my union with M. de Talleyrand gives me the right to bear, how the tender and sincere affection of that amiable friend has made me the happiest of women."

M. Van der Goes made Grand embark for the Cape immediately on receipt of Catherine's petition, and was rewarded with a gracious note from her, in which she assured him that "Monsieur de Talleyrand is as sensible as I am of your kind offices, and charges me to repeat to you all that I have already conveyed to you of his recognition, and his desire to give you proofs of his attachment and consideration."

But the anxieties of the Talleyrands with regard to Grand were not yet at an end, for scarcely had Grand set sail from Amsterdam when the truce of Amiens was broken. Alarmed at the thought that if his ship were captured en route the ghost of her past would once more appear in Paris to torment her, Catherine wrote again to Van der Goes, confiding her fears to him. Fortunately, he was able to set her mind at rest within a very short time by reporting that the newly appointed Councillor to the Regency at the Cape of Good Hope had safely reached his destination. So at last the past was comfortably buried and Catherine resolved that she would never taint the noble name of Talleyrand-Périgord by even so much as a breath of indiscretion.

Chapter Six

I

As Madame de Talleyrand Catherine preened herself like a bird of paradise. Looking at the world through rose-colored glasses she found it more exciting than ever. As Monsieur de Talleyrand's wife and the rightful queen of a salon crowded with the noblest and most brilliant men and women in Europe, she was at the height of her happiness and ambition.

On a certain evening every week she held a reception at the Hôtel Gallifet to which every person of distinction in Paris was invited. On such nights the Rue du Bac was lined with carriages and the great courtyard resembled the foyer of the Opéra during the intermissions of a gala performance. Singly or in pairs the guests passed through the open doorway and up the wide staircase decorated with flowers and lights, at the top of which, tall and beautiful and splendidly dressed, stood Madame de Talleyrand waiting to receive them, her husband, handsomely dressed in a suit of red velvet, at her side.

Every person who wished to keep within the charmed circle that surrounded the Minister of Foreign Affairs frequented these weekly receptions given by Madame de Talleyrand. Princes and princesses, ambassadors, men of letters, and messengers from foreign courts and governments all came. Even the envoy of Tunis, "a tall man in a turban, with very black mustaches, a gray robe trimmed with ermine over broidered red trousers," passed "through the double line of stars, orders and bedizened coats" one night to bow before the onetime Parisian courtesan.

Not all the entertainments given by the Minister of Foreign Affairs and his wife, however, were as ceremonious as these receptions held at the Hôtel Gallifet. At the Villa Neuilly, where

Catherine affected great state and scarcely moved a step without her attendant Orientals who burned incense before her, the amusements were far less formal and more in the nature of "at homes," to which only a select number of guests, often no more than twenty, were invited. During the meal an orchestra played Mozart softly in a secluded niche. Afterward the card tables were brought out or there was more music by talented guests, among them Madame de Laval, who often enchanted the company with her performance on the harp. Such an informal evening invariably came to an end with a few dances to a single violin.

But there were other nights when the company at dinner was much larger, often including some of England's most renowned statesmen and hostesses. Charles James Fox, the incomparable Whig, often dined at Neuilly during his stay in Paris at the time of the Peace of Amiens. He brought his wife with him, for Catherine had been on friendly terms with her in England during the years of her Revolutionary exile when Mrs. Fox was still the celebrated Bet Armistead.

To Neuilly, too, came Sir Elijah and Lady Impey, Lady Bessborough, and the Duchess of Cumberland. "I will not visit Madame Cabarrus," wrote Lady Bessborough in a letter to Lord Granville Leveson-Gower, referring to the lovely and notorious Theresia Tallien, "though I hope to see her to-morrow. Your native sense of justice makes you place Madame de Talleyrand in the same line, but power and marriage make so great a difference here that not visiting the latter would be reckoned a ridicule. . . ." In yet another letter to England, after a dinner at Neuilly, she wrote: "We arrived in good time. I met Lord Whitworth who handed us in and I was announced Ambassadrice d'Angleterre, which for a long time I could not rectify. I never saw anything so magnificent as the apartments, all perfumed with frankincense (*cela sent l'Évêque*)—and as soon as seventy-eight people (of which the company consisted) sat down, an immense glass at the end of the room slid away by degrees, and soft and beautiful music began to play in the midst of the jingle of glass and *vaisselle*. The dinner was, I believe, excellent, but from some awkwardness in the arrangements it was very difficult to get anything to eat. Madame de Talleyrand is like the Duchess of Cumberland and perfectly justifies the reason he gave for marrying her: *'Qu'elle emporte le prix de la bêtise.'* We waited a long while for dinner after we arrived and I continued meanwhile to get acquainted with Denon. . . . I desired him to sit by me at dinner, which he contrived to do, and amused me extremely. . . . I saw General Fox who was delighted to meet with anybody he knew. . . ."

Frequently fashionable writers were invited to Neuilly to entertain Monsieur and Madame de Talleyrand's guests by reading aloud from their works. Nepomucène Lemercier was the author on one such occasion, but he read his latest tragedy so badly and in such a dull unvaried voice that very soon the entire company was reduced to a state of exhaustion. Catherine tried to suppress her yawns, but at last, wearied and bored beyond endurance, she gave up the struggle and dozed lightly in her chair. Oblivious of the effect he had created, Lemercier continued to read to the end of the first act and then, pitching his voice several keys higher, began the second.

"*La scène est à Lyons,*" he announced shrilly.

Awakened from her half-sleep by the sudden change in his voice, Catherine sat bolt upright in her chair. "There now, my dear," she exclaimed, turning to her husband. "You see, I was right. You *would* call it the Sâone!"

The dramatist stopped dead in his recital, his mouth agape. Every eye looked with amused inquiry from Talleyrand to Catherine and for an instant the Minister of Foreign Affairs, too, gazed at his wife in perplexity. Then recollection dawned on him. "Ah, yes, of course, my dear, I remember," he said quietly. Then, with a twinkle in his little sinister eyes, he turned to the company and gravely explained the strange interruption. "When our carriage was passing over the bridge at Lyons a little while ago," he related, "Madame de Talleyrand asked me the name of the river that flowed beneath it. I told her it was the Sâone.

'The Sâone!' she cried. 'What a strange change of pronunciation! They call it the Seine in Paris!' "

Catherine joined gaily in the general laughter which greeted his narration of her Lyons sally. Good-natured and even-tempered, she was ready to participate even in merriment caused by a joke against herself. Her ear had not as yet become attuned to the malice in the laughter of Talleyrand's friends. Childishly delighted with her new state, it took some time for her to realize that in the eyes of the gentlemen in embroidered suits covered with orders, and the satin, velvet, and lace-gowned ladies, glittering with diamonds, she was but a common upstart, a vulgar, pretentious, silly creature of no consequence who had to be tolerated and treated with superficial courtesy because that was necessary if one wished to enjoy the fascinating company of her illustrious husband.

II

"Talleyrand wanted four things out of life. He wanted to be a bishop, a minister, a millionaire, and to marry a fool. He succeeded in all four." Such was General Macdonald's comment on Talleyrand after that gentleman had been a husband for twelve years. The good Macdonald was not in a position to know that a large part of Talleyrand's success in acquiring enormous wealth was due to the business acumen and charm of the fool the world said he had married.

Catherine's stupidity had become proverbial as far back as the early years of her married life. Though there were many who praised and admired her as one of the kindest and most gracious ladies of her time, a great many others, mainly women who loved Talleyrand, detested her and claimed to see in her only a vulgar parvenu of intolerable ignorance. "Her want of sense is such that it is impossible to disguise it," said some, and others declared that "silliness and vanity are stamped upon her face."

Above such clamors in society and at Court, the voice of friendly defense strove valiantly to make itself heard, praising her beauty and repeatedly asserting that she never said "anything approaching the absurd remarks which people have taken pleasure in imputing to her." But this was a small voice and easily deadened by the din of condemnation.

Fearing that he might be made to wear his wife's alleged stupidity "like a fool's cap," Talleyrand said nothing to refute it. He wrapped himself in a cloak of dignified silence and played the martyred husband to an audience of his lady friends. Occasionally he threw aside his cloak of silence and with some contemptuously cynical remark, made in very bad taste, blunted the shafts of ridicule he feared might strike him through his wife. For Talleyrand was an enigma—vain and witty, brutal and gallant, good-natured and unscrupulous, and as unaffected by another's pain as he was incapable of gratitude. So it was deliberately, knowing full well that it would be bandied about Paris, that he relieved himself of the following aphorism in a gathering of distinguished diplomats: "A clever woman often compromises her husband, a silly one only compromises herself." On another occasion, comparing Catherine with Madame de Staël, he said suavely: "One must have loved a genius to be able to appreciate the happiness of a fool." And to a friend he confided: "I married her because she was the greatest fool I could find." Yet he treated Catherine with courtesy and kindness, and invited no one to his table or his house who did not, on the surface, show her due respect and deference. Cynically he chuckled up his sleeve at a society that laughed hilariously in private at the alleged vulgarities and stupidites of a woman to whom, in public, and for the pleasure of his company, it paid cold but civil homage.

Mirabeau had once called Talleyrand a "vile base trickster." This he was—and more than this. Treacherous, hypocritical, and fundamentally indifferent to principles and the feelings of others, he had an insatiable genius for ensnaring and enslaving those who could be of use to him. He achieved his ends by

eloquence and intellect, by humor, and by almost unnatural
flattery. So in his web, knowing he could make use of her, he
had entangled Catherine. For Talleyrand realized quite plainly
that his wife was not the simple fool the world thought her to
be. Could a fool have induced him to marry her? Could a fool
have staged that cunning little play with the portrait on that
night of the great reception for the diplomatic corps?

But it suited his purpose that she should be thought a fool—
even by Bonaparte, who raised his voice in the general clamor,
declaring that in truth she was beautiful "but stupid and perfectly ignorant." Words, words—and what did the clamor of
words matter to Talleyrand since, despite her naïveté, facts spoke
more eloquently to him in proof of her sound common sense
and amazing business acumen.

Talleyrand venerated wealth and was not particularly squeam-
ish as to the manner in which he acquired it. So, when he found
that Catherine's charm and discretion and business ability could
be employed to good advantage in bringing certain unscrupulous transactions to fruition, he used her unblushingly. He
planned and schemed and played the piper, and Catherine, with
a Frenchwoman's shrewd instinct for making money, danced
to his tune like an intelligent and perfectly manipulated puppet.

Thus she helped "in a skilful organization of contraband
trading in the realms of the Czar," worked in conjunction
with a Russian woman, that brought a goodly sum to the Talleyrand coffers. On another occasion, by mediating on their behalf
for certain favors from her august husband, she obtained 400,-
000 francs from some Genoese merchants. And when Count
Bentheim Steinfurt desired to free his county from vassalage
to Hanover, which was occupied by France, he paid her 100,000
livres for helping him gain Talleyrand's promise to intercede with
Bonaparte.

Aware that his wife's passion for luxury and splendor was as
great as his own, Talleyrand ably and unscrupulously worked
behind the scenes, pulling a thousand little strings. And Catherine, dancing spiritedly though discreetly to his tune, helped

him by her charms and prudent judgment to amass a great fortune which included a sum of 4,000,000 francs paid him by the town of Hamburg in the hope that he would save the city from being handed over to France. Hamburg, unfortunately, met the fate it feared. But with the 4,000,000 francs Talleyrand bought and furnished one of the noblest palaces in Paris, the magnificent Hôtel Monaco in the Rue de Varenne.

III

At St. Cloud, on May 18, 1804, Bonaparte received the title of "Your Majesty" for the first time from the lips of Cambacérès, Second Consul and President of the Senate. He accepted it calmly, just as though he had been accustomed to it all his life. That day it was arranged that the formal coronation ceremony should take place before the year was out. Bonaparte, however, strenuously vetoed the suggestion that the Pope should place the diadem of sovereignty upon his head. He had found the crown of France lying on the ground and had taken it up on the point of his sword, he informed the Senate, and no hand but his own would place it on his head.

As he decreed, so it happened. On December 2, in the great cathedral of Notre-Dame, he crowned himself Emperor of France with his own hands. Pope Pius, who had accepted the invitation to be present at the coronation ceremony because of "the advantages and concessions to be gained by this gracious act," solemnly gave that which alone was required of him—his benediction. From that day the name of Bonaparte disappeared and that of Napoleon took its place—Napoleon I of France. In the newly created Empire there were no longer citizens and *cidevants* but only messieurs, mesdames, and aristocrats. And while that "red partridge" Fouché was nominated Minister of Police, Monsieur de Talleyrand was elevated to the high dignity of Grand Chamberlain.

Though he neither could nor would recognize the legality

of Talleyrand's marriage, during his stay in Paris Pope Pius was on moderately friendly terms with the newly appointed Grand Chamberlain. But he firmly refused to have Catherine presented to him. In his eyes there was no Madame de Talleyrand, but only a person, a onetime courtesan, of whom he greatly disapproved. If ever an occasion arose when he had, perforce, to allude to her, he studiedly and assiduously referred to her as *"questa donna"* or *"cette dame"*—that woman! This appellation delighted the scandalmongers of Paris and caused a new harvest of sarcasms about the wife of the Grand Chamberlain to ripen at Court and in fashionable society. Napoleon was not slow to note the effect created by the Pope's contemptuous designation and his disregard of the union he had practically forced upon Talleyrand. Indeed, the Emperor had long since regretted the part he had played in ensnaring Talleyrand into matrimony, for Catherine had lost his favor on the very first occasion that she appeared at the Tuileries as a bride.

"I hope that the good conduct of Citizen Talleyrand will cause the indiscretions of Madame Grand to be forgotten," he had welcomed her with characteristic ill-manner to her first Court.

"In that respect," she had answered him simply, her blue eyes innocently meeting his, "I cannot do better than follow the example of Citoyenne Bonaparte."

The impudence of the woman! That she dared rap him so sharply across the knuckles while gazing at him with so ingenuous an air! For that innocently administered reproof he had never forgiven her and from that time he treated her with cold indifference, often even "rudely." Now, with the Pope's disapproval to back him up, he determined once and for all to rid himself completely of all association with Talleyrand's marriage by refusing to receive Catherine at Court. But this was too much even for Talleyrand. Feeling that his "family pride was hurt," he flew to his wife's defense and insisted on her reception. When the Emperor remained adamant in his refusal, he tendered his resignation as a servant of the Crown. At this climax hasty negotiations were entered upon and finally Napoleon agreed to allow Madame de Talleyrand to appear at Court on the definite understanding that these appearances should be made "as seldom as possible." Talleyrand strictly adhered to this contract and so, too, did the Emperor, for even after she had become a princess he "never admitted her to the distinctions of the rank to which she was raised without making a difficulty about it."

Talleyrand was created a Prince of the Empire with the title of Prince de Bénévent two years after the coronation. "Eh, *mon Dieu,* you are mistaken. It isn't here, it is to Madame de Talleyrand you must present your compliments. Women are always delighted to be princesses," he told the courtiers who came to congratulate him on the new honor that had been conferred on him by the Emperor.

Soon after she became Princesse de Bénévent, Catherine had her portrait painted by Gérard. Standing with indolent grace before a fireplace, the leaping flames casting a crimson reflection on her sweeping white muslin empire gown, her tall figure lissom and graceful as a girl's, her golden hair crowning the loveliness of her gentle features, her head held proudly high, she made a perfect subject for the artist's brush.

At this time Catherine was forty-three. She carried her years lightly and was as beautiful as ever, though there were those in Paris who averred that her small retroussé nose gave her, curiously enough, a definite resemblance to Talleyrand.

Chapter Seven

I

Though Catherine's behavior before her marriage with Monsieur de Talleyrand was unquestionably open to censure, her conduct after that event was beyond reproach. The courtesan who had been the sport and plaything of many men became the devoted wife, zealously faithful to her husband and his interests, and prouder perhaps even than Talleyrand of the name she now bore. In 1803 when the two historic families of Talleyrand-Périgord and De Noailles became united by the marriage of Talleyrand's niece Mèlanie-Xavier de Périgord to Just de Noailles, Catherine was the only dissatisfied person. *"Cette alliance n'est point honorable pour nous,"* she declared. *"Car qu'est ce que c'est la famille de Noailles auprès de la mansion de Périgord."*

As swift as this astonishing metamorphosis in pride was the manner in which her personality changed. This was due in equal measure to the security of her position as wife of the Minister of Foreign Affairs and the attitude adopted toward her by the Court and the majority of Talleyrand's friends, particularly the women. Once fully conscious of their antagonism, she made no effort to hide the fact that she disliked them as cordially as they detested her, and she frequently showed her hatred in a manner neither dignified nor consistent with the elevated mien to which she aspired.

Fully convinced that her position gave her the right to treat those who displeased her with arrogant pride, she became haughty, headstrong, and full of self-importance. She had always loved luxury, splendor, and ostentation, but now, since beneath her rank and social veneer she still remained the middle-class daughter of Pierre Werlée, she grew pretentious and gave herself airs. The powerful guarantee of social security and consequence acted like an intoxicating wine on her senses. Her hauteur and pretentiousness became as proverbial as her beauty and stupidity. The naïvetés which had given "so strong a tinge of originality to all which she said or did," developed into eccentricities.

As a Princess of the Empire she affected an almost royal state, surrounding herself with a little court of pages and maids of honor, chamberlains, and mistresses of the robes. Though she often scorned ceremonial etiquette with impunity, she put great store on it in others. She was vain of her husband's armorial bearings which she displayed with inordinate pride, and she developed an overwhelming interest in genealogy, digging with almost ghoulish delight into the pedigrees of those who incurred her displeasure.

Yet there were times when the haughty princess could be as sweet and gracious as in the old days before marriage had made a great lady of her. She was as tender and kind to the people who showed her affection and friendship as she was arrogant to those whom she disliked.

Catherine was happy. Her *cher prince*, whom she loved with unwavering fidelity, was still the most sought-after man in the empire of France. Her salon was always crowded, and in the glitter of her title, her position, and her wealth, she found compensation for the disapproval of the Court and the bitter censure of the Emperor.

II

Talleyrand was constantly on guard against the mockery born of the scorn and arrogance with which Catherine met Napoleon's spite and society's criticism. Though when driven into a corner he seized the opportunity of "throwing back the ridicule which he felt was like to attack him, upon herself," for the present at any rate he stood by the mistake he had made and the woman he had married. "A haughty demeanor to those who ventured to laugh at him or her, extreme politeness, great social influence and political weight, a large fortune, unalterable patience under insult and much dexterity in taking his revenge, were the weapons with which he met the general condemnation."

At times, with his keen sense of the comic, he could not help feeling amused at Catherine's pretensions. But more often they irritated him. The grand seigneur, in spite of his sense of the ludicrous, often enough felt revolted by the silly airs of the parvenu. Yet, as always, he concealed his feelings and hid his annoyance behind a mask of dignified inscrutability. He was no longer in love with Catherine. He was patently unfaithful to her, amusing himself with endless amours. But he treated her with courtesy and saw to it that her position in his house was recognized with due respect.

For in truth, he still found her useful to him. He had the greatest respect for her shrewd understanding of the art of holding a salon, and her charm as a hostess was invaluable to him. Furthermore, her innate indolence exerted a powerful effect on his good nature. He was sure of her, sure that she would not disturb his delight in an easygoing existence with hysterical tantrums and violent scenes. For the time being, therefore, she suited him well enough.

But he was not really happy. Though he hid his feelings behind a disguise of indifference and habitual calm, though he never spoke of his married life and but rarely of his wife, his friends were quick to notice his unhappiness. Madame de Rémusat, lady-in-waiting to the Empress Josephine and Talleyrand's understanding and purely platonic friend, read in his eyes the bitter thoughts from which he tried to escape. "Public affairs helped him by giving him occupation," she declared, "and such time as they left on his hands he spent at the gaming-tables. Always surrounded by a numerous court, he gave his mornings to business, his evenings to the theatre and his nights to cards, never exposing himself to a tedious *tête-à-tête* with his wife, or to the dangers of solitude which would have afforded an opportunity for too serious reflection. Ever seeking distraction he never sought sleep until he had ensnared it by extreme fatigue."

Thus ran Madame de Rémusat's testimony of the ennui which Catherine caused her husband. It must be noted that it is not impartial testimony, for Madame de Rémusat and her husband, though they loved Talleyrand, never troubled to be friendly with his wife. They treated her with polite civility, but they never, even in her own salon, made more than a few conventional remarks to her on arrival or departure. Nevertheless, if Talleyrand was not quite so bored with Catherine as Madame de Rémusat would have us believe, she certainly no longer amused him.

Eagerly, then, he turned to a new diversion in his house—to Charlotte, the little daughter of an émigré who had died in exile in England. Anxious that she should be brought up in France, he confided her to the charge of France's Minister of Foreign Affairs, whose intimate friend he had been. Talleyrand was delighted with little Charlotte. He adopted her and bestowed his name on her and she came to live in his house. Catherine, who as a rule was jealous of the affection he showed to other people, opened her heart to the child, and mothered her as if she were her own daughter.

The happiness that the advent of the strange little girl brought to the Talleyrand home set the sharp tongues of the scandalmongers wagging mischievously. Some declared that the child was one of Talleyrand's numerous illegitimate offspring. Others declared with malicious conviction that she was the long-lost daughter of the onetime Madame Grand! But such rumors had no repercussions in the house of the Minister of Foreign Affairs where, her heart overflowing with tenderness as it always did toward those who loved her in return, Catherine spoiled and petted the little girl whom Talleyrand adored.

When, reclining on his very special ottoman, he granted his privileged audiences in the evenings after dinner, he always held Charlotte on his knees or close by his side. It was for her that he arranged children's balls and musical evenings at the mansion in the Rue d'Anjou-Saint-Honoré which he had given to Catherine as a marriage gift. These evenings, for which Talma, Crescenti, Madame Grassini and all the first artists of the day were engaged to give performances, became the talk of Paris. When a sudden attack of rheumatism made it necessary for him to "take the waters," Catherine and Charlotte and a small court, which included his confidential agent Blanc d'Hauterive, and that vivacious old lady Madame de Bonneuil, accompanied him to his favorite spa, Bourbon-l'Archambault.

At this time Charlotte was learning to read. Tears flowed at those reading lessons, for when Talleyrand frowned at the child or scolded her for stumbling over a word, Catherine, who still cried charmingly and with ease, wept copiously, her tears falling even faster than those of the little girl. But Catherine's weeping had long lost its effect on Talleyrand. He who once thought that no woman had ever looked so lovely as Catherine when she cried, now watched her unmoved, with calm *sangfroid*.

III

For the services which he rendered the Emperor in striking a great bargain with the Czar of Russia by the Treaty of Tilsit, Talleyrand was made Vice Grand Elector and Chief Chancellor. He now gave up the Ministry of Foreign Affairs and went to reside in splendor at his palace in the Rue de Varenne, Faubourg Saint-Germain. It was called the Hôtel Monaco, and he had acquired it through Catherine's help and the City of Hamburg's bribe of 4,000,000 francs. Foreigners called the Hôtel Monaco "the little court." Here all the state and ceremony, elegance, manners, and practices of a royal palace were observed. Talleyrand surrounded himself with an enormous suite. Courtiers flattered him, hangers-on fawned on him, and servants, stewards, and chamberlains danced attendance on his needs and on the needs of his princess, who herself was followed by a train of attendants, pages, maids of honor, and mistresses of the robes.

To the Hôtel Monaco to pay their respects to the illustrious Vice Grand Elector came every person of rank and consequence, ambassadors and their wives, foreign princes and princesses, indeed, all the most distinguished people of Europe then in Paris. The reception rooms were always crowded and there was ever a small coterie of women present of whom Talleyrand "had in general been rather the lover than the friend." Among the many women who frequented the "little court" were the Duchesse de Luynes, the Princesse de Vaudemout, and Talleyrand's much attached and faithful Vicomtesse de Laval; clever Aimée de Coigny, the first Duchesse de Fleury who had married Montrond; good Madame de Rémusat, trying "by the sweat of her brow to say something clever"; Mesdames de Bellegarde "whose only claim to importance in society was their extreme licence of speech"; Madame de Souza, wife of the ambassador to Portugal, who had been the Vice Grand Elector's inamorata in the days when she was Madame de Flahaut; and the Countess Tyskiewitz, a Polish lady with a glass eye who had met Talleyrand in Warsaw before Tilsit, fell passionately in love with him, and followed him to Paris. Though her husband's lady friends treated her coldly, greeting her only when they arrived or left her salon and but seldom addressing more than a dozen banal remarks to her, Catherine scorned them and was happy in her arrogance. For she too, like some of them, was a real princess and, despite their jealousy, the queen of Talleyrand's little court. Although they considered her an intruder, as the wife of the Vice Grand Elector they had to pay her civil respect whether they liked it or not. That was all she expected of them.

At this time Catherine was still very beautiful. She loved clothes and jewels, always dressed magnificently, and spent many hours of each day in the company of her milliner, her hairdresser, her jeweler, and her dressmaker. She did not read much, did very little fancywork, paid few visits, and seldom went to Court. Yet life was never dull for her. The luxuries of being a princess, the company of Charlotte and a few sincere friends, the theater, shopping, driving in the Bois, the splendid receptions at which she played hostess, completely satisfied her needs. She was the head of the charmed circle that gathered around her distinguished husband.

She looked beautiful on those evenings of the great assemblies, magnificently gowned and with flowers or pearls and precious stones in her still golden hair. Regally and rather stiffly she sat in her chair. She did not speak much. It was difficult for her to shine conversationally in the presence of so unrivaled a talker as her husband. "If Monsieur de Talleyrand's conversation could be bought, I should ruin myself on it!" Madame de Staël had once said in the days when Talleyrand was still her friend.

Though many years had passed since then, his tongue had lost none of its wit. Small wonder that, never a sparkling conversationalist at best, Catherine was often reduced to silence by the firework display of Talleyrand and his guests. When she did speak, Talleyrand seldom listened to what she said. Sometimes, with her unaffected artlessness she made quite amusing remarks, but too often—as on the occasion when the Princess Dolgorouki, covered in magnificent jewels, arrived at a reception at the Hôtel Monaco—he found her ingenuous candor embarrassing.

"Oh, madame, what beautiful diamonds!" Catherine had exclaimed that night in rapture at the sight of her guest's display of jewels. "How happy you must be to possess them!"

"If you expressed a wish to have some like them," replied the Princess Dolgorouki, "I am sure the Prince de Talleyrand would be delighted to make you a present of them."

"But, *mon Dieu*, madame, you forget!" cried Catherine. "Do you imagine I have married the Pope?"

Chapter Eight

I

Regularly each year when the Paris weather became unpleasantly warm, the Talleyrands forsook their town house for the Château of Valençay, an estate in Berry which Talleyrand had bought the year after his marriage, and which, since he delighted in playing the role of a country squire, held infinite charms for him.

Catherine loved Valençay. She loved it with an almost religious fervor. Here she was not merely a great lady but a veritable queen. The grandly austere château, part convent part fortress, with its rambling cloisters, sunny salons, high towers, and deep moat, was her royal palace. The wide-flung vista of valley, parklands, and forest were the limits of her kingdom.

Always, at the first sign of spring in Paris, her thoughts turned like homing birds to Valençay. Spring with its bursting buds and young wet leaves elated her senses. The cooing of the wood pigeons in the elms of her château in Berry sounded as sweet as the song of nightingales. She loved to wander down the long lilac-scented alleys of the park or drive through the forest clearings, where a fleeting glimpse of a roebuck or a deer sent her into ecstasies of delight.

But perhaps her greatest affection for Valençay was inspired by the fact that here, occasionally, she could be alone with her *cher prince* for as long as half an hour at a time—a joy that seldom came to her in Paris. Though in later years he rarely addressed a remark to her as she sat beside him indolently plying her embroidery needle—he would bury himself securely behind a copy of the *Moniteur*—these rare moments at Valençay, alone with him and undisturbed, were the happiest of her life. How proud she felt and with what a possessive air she looked at Talleyrand when a guest appeared suddenly on the terrace and found them there sitting quietly together.

All through the long summer the château was filled with visitors, illustrious, social, political, and literary personages. The pleasures arranged for their entertainment were many and varied. Sometimes too, "in all the majesty of stiffened silks and fluttering plumes," Catherine played hostess at a dinner to the maire and the curé and all the authorities of the district. In the eyes of these provincials she was a very great lady indeed, gracious and charming and much respected for her many kindnesses to the poor and her generosity in establishing a school for a dozen girls at Valençay.

But perhaps of all her neighbors the noble family of De Rostaing loved her best. Monsieur de Rostaing had been prominent in the Royalist rising in La Vendée in 1795, but now, old and forgotten, he lived with his family in retirement and in poor circumstances in a small cottage near the Talleyrand château. From the very first Catherine's warm heart had been touched by the ill fortune which had befallen this family of high birth. Generously she came to their aid, doing everything in her power to make the lives of Monsieur and Madame de Rostaing easier and pleasanter. Their two daughters, girls of marked character and gentility, she took under her special care. She had them educated at her expense, and when they were old enough, introduced them into society.

A calm lay on Valençay and there was nothing to warn Catherine of the approach of a rising gale. Happily she spent enchanting summers in her beloved château. There was nothing to warn her that one day she would be forever parted from it, nor that, strange as it might seem, her fate was bound up with that of the Emperor, whose covetous eyes were fixed on the kingdom of Spain.

II

The Spanish drama, which was to start a new chapter in the Napoleonic era, began at Fontainebleau in October, 1807, with a secret convention between France and Spain, of which the ostensible issue was the partition of Portugal. Actually, however, Napoleon was scheming for the military occupation of Spain by peaceful means, his object to place his brother Joseph on the throne. Talleyrand was bitterly opposed to the series of diabolical plots by which the Emperor planned to get Spain into his power and make it a dependency of France. "This is a base intrigue. It is a blunder which will never be repaired," he declared in a heated argument with his Emperor.

But in spite of Talleyrand's resistance French troops did enter Spain in accordance with the terms of the secret Fontainebleau Convention and marched toward Lisbon. They met no opposition, but at their approach the royal family of Portugal fled to Brazil in the Portuguese fleet. Gradually and peacefully, Napoleon's troops occupied the most strategic positions in Spain. It was suddenly borne upon Charles IV of Spain that his country had been betrayed to France by his minister Godoy. Revolts broke out throughout the length and breadth of Spain. The Spanish people, roused to fury by Godoy's treachery, demanded not only the head of Godoy, Prince of the Peace, but also the abdication of their king in favor of his son Ferdinand, Prince of Asturias.

These domestic quarrels in Spain suited Napoleon's schemes admirably. He left Paris after a cold parting from Talleyrand, who more bitterly than ever opposed the Spanish plot, and arrived at Bayonne. There he laid a well-baited trap into which, by a series of unblushing intrigues, he lured first Charles IV and then his son Ferdinand. He compelled them both to surrender all claim to the Spanish throne. This work done, he allowed the timid Charles and his queen Maria Luisa to depart to the Château de Compiègne and afterward to Italy, packed Ferdinand of Asturias off to France, and prevailed upon a small number of Spanish grandees to elect Joseph Bonaparte to the vacant throne.

It was Talleyrand, who had so strongly objected to the Spanish conspiracy, whom the Emperor now chose as gaoler of the Spanish Infantes, Ferdinand of Asturias, his young brother Carlos, and their uncle Don Antonio; and it was Talleyrand's own Château of Valençay that he selected as a prison for his unwilling guests.

"See that the rooms are ready; prepare the bed and table linen and kitchen utensils," Napoleon wrote with imperial command to his Vice Grand Elector. "I wish these Princes to be received without exterior pomp, but decently and with attention, and that you should do your best to amuse them. If you have a theater at Valençay, there would be no harm in getting some comedians to come down. You might have Madame de Talleyrand there and four or five women. If the Prince of Asturias should fall in love with some pretty woman, and the fact were known, there would be no objection to it as it would be one more way of keeping a watch on him. It is of the greatest importance that the Prince of Asturias should not commit any blunder. . . . I have determined to send him to a country seat and to surround him with pleasure and with supervision. . . . For yourself, your mission is sufficiently honorable. To receive three illustrious persons and amuse them is quite in the character of the nation and of your rank. . . ."

Talleyrand was infuriated by this message. Only too well did he read between the lines. It was to repay him for his antagonism to the Spanish plot that the Emperor now labored to humble and discredit him in the eyes of Europe. By appointing him custodian of the dethroned prince, Napoleon was obviously planning to keep him well out of affairs in Paris. Furthermore, and with insult added to injury, there could be no mistake about the insolently cynical innuendoes directed at his wife and the part she should play at Valençay. Though he boiled inwardly with rage and indignation, he could do nothing. His hands were tied. There was no way out of this embarrassing situation.

"I will respond with my best endeavors to the confidence with which your Majesty honors me," he replied with dignified irony to Napoleon's communication. "Madame de Talleyrand left last night to give the preliminary orders. The Château is amply furnished with cooks, china and linen of all kinds. The

Princes shall have every pleasure which the bad season permits.
I will give them Mass every day, a park to walk in, a well-
cleared forest, though with little game in it, horses, numerous
meals and music. There is no theatre, and it would be more
than difficult to find actors. However, there will be enough
women for the Princes to dance with if it amuses them. . . ."

A few days later the princes of Spain—Ferdinand of Asturias,
an intellectually undeveloped young widower of twenty-four,
his young brother Carlos, and their uncle Don Antonio—arrived
at Valençay in a clumsy, old-fashioned stage coach. They were
followed almost immediately by their suite of twenty people,
which included their ecclesiastical mentor and guide, Canon
Escoïquitz, and the dashing Duc de San Carlos, a merry courteous gentleman of fashion with a reputation for subtlety,
finesse, and daring in amorous intrigues.

III

Catherine was proud to have such distinguished guests as the
scions of Spanish royalty under her roof. She received the Infantes at Valençay with charming hospitality. Talleyrand, too,
did what he could for his unwelcome visitors and since he had
been granted 75,000 francs a year by the state for their main-
tenance, spared no expense in giving them all the splendor and
luxury he thought necessary to make their captivity as pleasant as possible.

The Château of Valençay took on the appearance of a Cas-
tilian palace; the servants were dressed in livery in the Spanish
colors; and the yellow and red flag of Spain streamed in the
breeze from the central tower. With luxury, entertainment, and
discretion, Talleyrand and his princess tried to pacify the angry
and unhappy Infantes who had been so basely cheated of their
country. The famous Castro was especially engaged to enchant
them into contentment by playing his guitar in the shrubberies;
one of the Prince de Condé's old guard, a man named Aubry,

taught them to shoot so that they might enjoy the pleasures of deer hunting in the forest of Gâtine; grooms taught them to ride on horseback for the first time; they went fishing; they danced the bolero and fandango on the terrace, and made music with Catherine and her women guests in the drawing rooms.

A large number of elegant and highborn ladies, including the Duchesse de Gênes, the two Mesdames Bellegarde, and the very beautiful Genoese Madame de Brignoli, had been invited to Valençay, and the Château gave the illusion of a court. Nothing was wanting to make the princes happy in their gilded cage. Spain had to become for them a "forgotten country." Also, they were to be kept uninformed of the grave events in the Peninsula.

Diplomatically the Prince de Bénévent and his princess covered the chains of captivity with the flowers of pleasure. Talleyrand even attempted to educate the two young princes, but the education "which began in the library gradually sank to the level of a picture book." The twenty-four-year-old widower, Ferdinand of Asturias, was an extraordinarily simple creature, his young brother Carlos a mere child. They preferred the clamors of a fair to the peace of a library, and enjoyed buying children's toys at a booth and playing childish games far more than studying great books with their host. Fireworks, too, sent them into wild delight, and when a poor person begged alms of them they gave him a doll instead.

Talleyrand found the custodianship of the young princes and their suite wearisome and embarrassing. He heaved a great sigh of relief when in the middle of August and at the request of Napoleon—who had need of him at the Erfurt Conference—he was at last able to set out for Nantes and later for Paris. He left his wife and her ladies at Valençay, however, "so that the Château should not suddenly appear monastic."

For the gradual change which took place in the hearts of the Infantes, Catherine's attentiveness as a hostess was almost as much responsible as Talleyrand's adroitness in managing their feelings. In a short time they grew deeply enamored of Valençay, and with youthful fickleness often declared that they preferred it infinitely to the solemn splendor and awe-inspiring pomp of the Spanish court.

Ferdinand in particular was highly contented, for he had found an amiable diversion in a love affair with one of Catherine's young ladies. And no sooner did Talleyrand leave for Nantes than that dazzling Don Juan, the Duc de San Carlos, began to enliven his exile by laying siege to his hostess' heart.

The company of the Spanish duke and the homage he paid her delighted Catherine. It pleased her to think that though she was nearing fifty a young and dashing man of the world still found her desirable and beautiful. The years had not dulled the keen edge of her appetite for flattery and compliments. But the old days of impudent imprudence were over. She was no longer Madame Grand but Madame de Talleyrand, Princesse de Bénévent, a great lady who was in no mood for indiscretions that might taint the noble names she bore with so much pride.

Tactfully she repulsed San Carlos' more ardent pleadings and won his friendship instead, a friendship which committed her to nothing more than a pretty flirtation and the joy of listening, happy as a debutante, to the enchanting nonsense he poured into her ears. But the scandalmongers of Paris found such a relationship between the ladykilling Duc de San Carlos and his hostess quite incomprehensible. Malicious tongues began to hint that the Princesse de Talleyrand was playing her part at Valençay "in a manner much more calculated to please the Emperor than her husband." When she left Valençay with the last of the fine weather—a beloved Valençay which she was destined never to see again—and returned to Paris, these rumors of a liaison were confirmed without further qualms. Frequently during the months that followed Canon Escoïquitz "in a cassock with huge trousers and the *grand cordon* of Charles III over his shoulder," came to the Hôtel Monaco or the mansion in the Rue d'Anjou-Saint-Honoré to pay his respects. Still more often the Duc de

San Carlos was present in her salon, charming the ladies with his courtly attentions. Gossip, battening on these visits, became garrulous. Soon everyone was saying that the Duc de San Carlos was Catherine de Talleyrand's lover.

IV

Napoleon returned to Paris after his victory at Wagram fully decided upon his divorce from Josephine. The proceedings put him in a bad mood and he vented his ill-humor on the Ministers of his Council and the members of his Court. Talleyrand alone, during these anxious days, appeared to him a veritable tower of strength.

"There is no one but Talleyrand with whom I can talk," he declared repeatedly. So once again he turned in friendship to the man he had banished from his intimacy at the beginning of the Spanish drama. For Talleyrand strongly supported the Emperor in his desire for a divorce, urging instead a powerful matrimonial alliance with an archduchess. The Prince de Bénévent had never forgiven Josephine for the part she had played in forcing him to give his name to Catherine Grand. . . .

In December, 1809, the Emperor's marriage was annulled. Four months later he married his Austrian archduchess, Marie Louise. In Paris great festivities were held in honor of the wedding. The city overflowed with distinguished visitors and as usual Talleyrand's salon was crowded. Like moths around a candle, the old charmed circle of feminine admirers fluttered about him. The Vicomtesse de Laval was faithful as ever; so was Madame de Souza; the Comtesse Tyskiewitz, whose glass eye "made her profile look so strange," brought her niece, the Countess Potoçka; Madame de Rémusat came too, and so did the Comtesse de Boigne.

But the Duchess of Courland, whose lovely, talented daughter Dorothéa had recently married Talleyrand's dull and uninteresting nephew Edmond de Périgord, was the most constant satellite among the great ladies of the Faubourg Saint-Germain. At the age of forty-five she was still very beautiful. Often she would come to Talleyrand's salon long after midnight to show him a new jewel or a ball dress that she was wearing, "just as a girl of twenty might have done." He was passionately in love with her.

Yet Catherine still occupied the place of honor in the magic circle about her husband. Haughtier than ever, she treated the ladies of his "elderly seraglio" with frigid civility, often with studied rudeness. For though she set great store by etiquette, she sometimes considered even ordinary politeness beneath her dignity in her dealings with those she disliked. Her pretensions made her insupportable to the coterie of Monsieur de Talleyrand's feminine admirers, and these ladies seldom called at the Hôtel Monaco unless they felt quite sure of finding him there to protect them from her airs and graces.

Pride and arrogance often made her overstep the bounds of good manners in these days, as on the memorable occasion when she went out for a walk at an hour fixed for a reception at her house. When the guests arrived they were naïvely informed by the solitary lady-in-waiting who received them in the drawing room that "Her Highness, seduced by a ray of sunshine, had gone out for a turn in the Bois." Patiently but in simmering anger, they awaited the return of their hostess. At last she arrived. Smiling and gracious, she entered the room with a rustle of silk. And she offered neither apology nor excuse for having kept her guests waiting more than an hour.

Talleyrand's pleasure in his wife had ceased years ago. There was no longer room for her in his life. He found her neither amusing in private nor particularly helpful in his salon. Though he still treated her with distant but dignified courtesy in public, he assiduously avoided being alone with her and divided his time more and more among his public duties, gambling, and the company of his "elderly seraglio," with the Duchess of Courland as his favorite companion. Occasionally, it is true, Catherine was seen at the gambling parties given by the Comtesse Tyskiewitz, which Talleyrand attended more frequently, but she never went to Madame de Laval's, where he and the Duchess of Courland were regular visitors.

Yet, though her husband and the Faubourg Saint-Germain treated her coldly, the latter neither expecting nor desiring visits from her, and though she appeared but seldom at Court, she was happy. Fate had elevated her to high rank and the honor of a great name. She was a princess and very rich. In spite of her unpopularity among her husband's women admirers, her salon was always crowded. She had the companionship of Charlotte, who was "growing quite a big girl and more and more lovable," and she possessed a few good friends, among them the kindly Millin, amateur of the arts, who flattered, admired, and paid her gallant court.

And still the Spanish princes lived in gilded captivity at Valençay and still, more often than ever, the Canon Escoïquitz and the Duc de San Carlos were seen in Catherine's salon. Louder and more insistent grew the rumor of the supposed liaison between the Duc and the upstart wife of the Prince de Talleyrand. At last it reached the ears of the Emperor himself.

Napoleon was in a quarrelsome mood. Affairs in the Peninsular War had been going badly for France, and Talleyrand's persistent opposition to his ceaseless struggles for conquest deeply incensed him. Angry scenes took place between them continually, and the Emperor had reached the stage where he was ready to use any weapon on which he could lay hands to bring Talleyrand down a peg or two. The rumored affair between Catherine and the Spanish duke seemed to him a splendid instrument for an offensive. He chose a levee as the most suitable time to speak of this matter to his Vice Grand Elector. "It seems to me that Spain has brought us both bad luck, Monsieur de Talleyrand," he said mockingly before a host of courtiers. "Why did you not tell me that the Duc de San Carlos was your wife's lover?"

"I did not think it redounded either to Your Majesty's honor or mine," came the crushing reply. "In truth, sire, it would have been better, both for Your Majesty's glory and mine, that there never had been anything to do with these Spanish princes." Not a muscle had moved in Talleyrand's face. Only his snakelike eyes gleamed with intense emotion as they stared coldly and fixedly into those of the Emperor.

Without a word Napoleon turned on his heel and walked away. A volcanic rage set his body on fire. *Mon Dieu,* but that Talleyrand was insufferable! What did he take himself for that he dared to teach his Emperor a lesson? He would be made to suffer for those words. He would be made to suffer.

The Emperor had his revenge. But it was Catherine rather than Talleyrand who suffered his retaliation. Not only did he close the doors of the Tuileries to her forever, he banished the Duc de San Carlos from her salon and, by consigning him to the boredom of exile in the sleepy little town of Bourg-en-Bresse, deprived her of a sentimental and delectable companionship.

Chapter Nine

I

The breach in the relationship of the Emperor and his Vice Grand Elector widened till it assumed the appearance of a chasm. Their quarrels grew more bitter and more frequent. Not only did the Emperor heap reproaches on Talleyrand's head but now he began to delve into the past and ask awkward questions. How had Talleyrand managed to amass so great a fortune? What were his winnings at the gaming tables? How much had he made by speculation on the stock exchange? Digging into bygone scandals the Emperor discovered how, years ago, Catherine had received 400,000 francs from some Genoese merchants for commercial favors she had obtained for them from her husband, and what was more, that Talleyrand himself had received a bribe of 4,000,000 francs from the town of Hamburg, which he had spent to buy and furnish the Hôtel Monaco in the Rue de Varenne.

This was too much for Napoleon. The last drop of bitterness had fallen into his cup of anger and now it overflowed. At all costs he would rid himself of the perfidious and mercenary Talleyrand. With coarse brutality he dismissed his Vice Grand Elector from office and forced him to give up the magnificent Hôtel Monaco. Talleyrand listened to the Emperor's fuming denunciation of his venality and treachery with serenity as he leaned against a console. He made no reply to the thundered accusations hurled at him. Only when he took his departure did he express his contempt and disdain of the Emperor Napoleon in one immortal sentence: "What a pity that so great a man has been so badly brought up," he muttered as he limped through the courtiers on his way out of the room.

Despite his dismissal he continued to present himself at Court, but with a reserve so haughty that it could not in any way be mistaken for humility. Under compulsion he had abandoned the Hôtel Monaco, but very soon he bought and furnished a mansion in the Rue Saint-Florentin, near the Tuileries, an elegant though much smaller dwelling than the palace in the Rue de Varenne. Though he was no longer in office, all Paris flocked to his salon where, at the head of two rows of armchairs, Catherine still tranquilly did the honors. For Talleyrand, the grand seigneur and "eternal Bishop of Autun," who had begun his brilliant career in the far-off days of Louis XVI and had been in turn President of the Constituent Assembly that organized the French Revolution, Minister of Foreign Affairs, Grand Chamberlain, and Vice Grand Elector under the Empire, was still the first man in France in political skill and the art of diplomacy. Still all Europe recognized his genius.

II

During the early part of the year 1811 Catherine was far from well. With the first real warm weather in June she set out for Aix-les-Bains in the hope of recovering from her "obstinate ebullition." On her arrival at her destination she wrote to her kind and understanding friend Millin, amateur of the arts, describing the impressions of her journey to him. In its simplicity and naturalness this letter reveals the real Catherine, an ingenuous creature who too often hid her true personality behind a screen of arrogant pretentiousness.

"I am enchanted, monsieur, with the country I have passed through," she told Millin. "As far as Geneva the views are picturesque or severe, and sometimes frightful. But the approach to Geneva is enchanting. Nothing can equal the beautiful lake that surrounds it; the pretty country houses scattered about make charming views. The summit of Mont Blanc and the glaciers make an imposing crown to these smiling scenes, which one can never grow weary of admiring. As to the town of Aix, monsieur, which one might easily mistake for a wretched village, there is nothing attractive about it, but the environs are varied and picturesque. There are some charming views. The Lake of Bourget has also some merit of its own; it is enclosed by rocks and mountains, it has not the smiling aspect of Geneva, but there is something somber and melancholy about it: the one invites joy, and the other gentle reveries. . . ."

Aix-les-Bains speedily cured her of her "obstinate ebullition" and she returned to Paris. But in the early autumn she left it again and set out for the Baths of Bourbon-l'Archambault. On this journey, in a sudden mood of eccentricity, she commited her first imprudent act since her marriage to Talleyrand. Rashly she abandoned the straight road to Bourbon-l'Archambault for a circuitous route which, passing through Bourg-en-Bresse, enabled her once again to see her old friend the Duc de San Carlos.

Ever since his banishment she had kept up a tender, friendly correspondence with him, a correspondence which of necessity had to be conducted with the strictest secrecy, for the Emperor, and Talleyrand at his request, had sternly forbidden her to have any association whatsoever with the Spaniard. Canon Escoïquitz, however, had proved a discreet intermediary and with his help she had managed to keep in close touch with her exiled friend. To mitigate the tedium of his banishment she wrote him affectionate, gossipy letters in which she told him about the newest plays at the theater; about the actors at the Français, which she frequented regularly; about books and music and dancing and all the latest society chatter in Paris. She spoke of her home too, of her husband's ability at billiards, of the splendid progress Charlotte was making, and of a new gown or jewel that she had bought. Until that autumn day when a sudden whim made her take the long road to Bourg-en-Bresse, the haughty princess, who so highly prized the name she bore, had behaved with the greatest discretion and perception in this friendship.

Perhaps the fact that Talleyrand spent the greater part of this early autumn at St. Germain where the Duchess of Courland had taken a small château had a great deal to do with Catherine's mood of defiance and the eccentricity of her conduct. Scenes between Talleyrand and Catherine had been frequent of late. She irritated him, and his attentions to other women often drove her into dark moods of querulous jealousy. The tranquil pleasures of home life had long ceased to exist for both of them.

Only at the Duchess of Courland's château at St. Germain, a quaint place that had once been the hunting box of Henry IV, did Talleyrand find the peace and companionship his nature demanded. The Duchess was enchanting, her guests, Madame de Laval, the Saxon Countess Kielmannsegge, and the good Nesselrode, were congenial; and he spent many hours in the open, riding clumsily on a small chestnut mare "under the tall oaks of the forest and through the fields of roses, swinging his cane the while, faster or slower, according to the speed of his thoughts."

At St. Germain one August evening Talleyrand received a letter from the Duke de Rovigo informing him of the secret meeting Catherine had had with the Duc de San Carlos at Bourg-en-Bresse. The Emperor, declared the Duke, was extremely angry at the Princesse de Talleyrand's disregard of his command and, as a result of her behavior, was planning to banish her to her estate at Pont-de-Sains. Furthermore, the Emperor had declared that if Talleyrand "could not control his wife's movements" better in future, "the same fate would befall him." The Duke conveyed his unpleasant news in the most painstakingly diplomatic manner. But even his polite words could not hide the contemptible meanness of Napoleon's petty tyranny. Calmly Talleyrand replied to the timely warning, changing and rewriting his reply several times before finally affixing his seal. At one o'clock in the morning he dispatched his answer by the same gendarme who had brought the Duke's communication. At five he himself departed in a carriage for Paris.

That same evening he was back at St. Germain again and in excellent spirits, highly satisfied with his day's work. And well he might be, for he had won a victory over Napoleon in interceding successfully with him on Catherine's behalf. Instead of banishment to Pont-de-Sains she was allowed to return to Paris, but on the strict understanding that she remain quietly and in semiretirement in her hôtel. These restrictions were of a temporary nature, and were withdrawn soon afterward.

And meanwhile Talleyrand continued to spend most of his time at St. Germain. The Duchess was so enchanting.

III

On a bleak February night in the year 1812 a dense congestion of carriages and a great throng of people massed in the environs of the Tuileries, for in the theater of this palace, brilliantly decorated and illuminated and turned into a ballroom, the Queen of Naples was holding her Great Quadrille. Two thousand magnificently dressed guests—the men in splendid uniforms and glittering decorations, the women with diamonds and pearls in their hair—filled the great hall, while fifteen hundred eager spectators sat in the boxes. When Napoleon and his Austrian archduchess had taken their places in the royal box, the pleasures of the evening began. First came a square dance for four couples. The Empress led off with the Prince of Neufchâtel, and with them danced Queen Hortense, Marshal Duroc, Madame Davout, General Nansouty, the Countess Eroy, and Prince Aldobrandini.

No sooner had the contradance come to an end than the great treat of the evening was staged, an interlude portraying the splendors of a new Rome, re-created by France. First came a procession of twelve men dressed to represent twelve constellations. They were followed by a body of Roman lictors, who in turn were followed by a band of men representing light stars.

Suddenly the music changed tempo, and a tall and lovely

woman stepped into the light and began to dance. In her diary the following day the Countess Kielmannsegge who was present at the Great Quadrille recorded the appearance of this enchanting apparition: "Then followed Iris (Madame Le Grand) in a white and blue robe, a coloured shawl in her hand and a necklace of coloured stones about her throat. She danced first the shawl dance and then a solo, very simply and with grace. Her lovely fair hair adorned her beauty." . . . On this night when the Princesse de Talleyrand—the Countess somewhat incorrectly called her Madame Le Grand—danced in the presence of the Emperor, the Queen of Naples, and her three thousand guests, she had but two months to go before celebrating her fiftieth birthday. Yet she could still dance with elegance and grace, and was delightful to look at in the warm loveliness of her mature beauty.

A few months later Talleyrand and Catherine went to take the waters at Bourbon-l'Archambault. They were on friendly terms again. "Madame de Talleyrand," the prince wrote in a letter from the spa in June, "reads to me every night in French."

Catherine was far from well on their return to Paris. A digestive ailment caused her much suffering and discomfort. During the two years that followed, ill-health took sad toll of her figure and complexion. She began to put on weight. Her lissom body lost some of its suppleness and indolent grace, and her chiseled features something of their delicacy. The pink and white texture of her skin often became transfused with a hectic flush, and in her abundant golden hair nestled, though inconspicuously it is true, a few fine threads of gray. Yet serenely, "wearing the remains of her great beauty like a crown," she sat at the end of the long row of armchairs in Talleyrand's salon and with dignity and grace did the honors of the Hôtel Saint-Florentin.

It was here, early in 1814, that suddenly one day she was brought face to face with a ghost from the past and the memory of a night when the most beautiful courtesan and the handsomest man in Paris dined strangely together for the first time and the last. The ghost that confronted her was Edouard Dillon whose niece, the Comtesse de Boigne, brought him to the Hôtel Saint-Florentin to call on Talleyrand and his princess. Dillon, who had not set foot in Paris for twenty-seven years, was still handsome, still most gallant.

As the carriage trundled on its way to the Rue Saint-Florentin, Dillon sat wrapped in silence beside his niece. Ever and again a smile touched his lips for an instant.

"Are they very amusing, those thoughts of yours, *mon oncle?*" the Comtesse de Boigne asked him at last.

"Very," he replied laconically, and a moment later he added: "We live in a strange world indeed."

"Surely not a very profound remark from a man like Handsome Edouard Dillon!"

He laughed and looked at his niece amusedly. "Ah well, since I see that you are consumed with curiosity," he teased, "I shall put you out of your agony, my dear. Besides, the contrast between this visit and the only one I paid formerly to the Princesse de Talleyrand is so amusing, that I cannot resist telling you of my last and only interview with her." Quietly, then, like a man looking at his lost youth through a telescope, he spoke of the night that he had dined with the loveliest courtesan in Paris and she had sat at table "naked an unashamed, like a second Eve before any dress material had been invented."

"It will be amusing to see what her attitude will be towards you," his niece said.

"It will be curious," he answered.

A few minutes later they were announced at the Hôtel Saint-Florentin and entered the salon. Catherine received them charmingly. By not so much as the flicker of an eyelash did she reveal the thoughts that flashed through her mind when Dillon was presented to her. She greeted him as if she had never before set eyes on him. Then she invited the Countess to take the seat at her side and Dillon, bowing, moved slightly behind his niece's chair.

For the first few minutes the conversation concerned itself entirely with the weather, but at last, adroitly, Catherine changed the subject by admiring the bonnet the Comtesse de Boigne was wearing. It was charming, she declared, quite the most becoming bonnet that she had seen for a long time. How perfectly it suited the wearer! But then, of course, the Comtesse had such beautiful hair. Was it very long, and did it reach far below the shoulders? Indeed! But how enchanting! And now suddenly, turning her head and looking at Dillon with innocent naïveté and perfect gravity, she said: "Monsieur Dillon, you like beautiful hair, do you not?"

IV

"I shall have war with Russia on grounds which lie beyond human possibilities, because they are rooted in the case itself," Napoleon told Metternich in the autumn after his marriage to Marie Louise. Two years later he had his war. For a month he waited with his army in Moscow for the surrender of Czar Alexander. It did not come. Now it dawned on him that if he was to avoid the grueling horror of a Russian winter, he must retire immediately. The retreat began, but it began too late. He had to pay for the greatest error of his career with half a million men.

Back in Paris, he turned again to Talleyrand, whose venality and deceit he despised but of whose diplomatic skill he now had great need. He offered him the portfolio of Foreign Affairs. Talleyrand refused. This man who had already sold the Directory to the Consulate and the Consulate to the Empire was much too busy negotiating to sell the Emperor Napoleon to his enemies. His mansion in the Rue Saint-Florentin had become the center of anti-Napoleonic intrigue. Here, secretly, he gathered about him the leaders of the discontented faction in France, a faction wearied by war and surfeited with glory, which clamored for peace and security and the return of the Bourbons.

But Talleyrand had other worries besides those of political

intrigue. A series of domestic troubles now came to disturb his mind more than politics ever had done. For at this time, when he was sixty years of age, a specter of a man limping on one leg, he fell prey to an unquenchable passion for Dorothéa, the young and beautiful wife of his nephew Edmond de Périgord and the daughter of his most ardent and recent adorer, the Duchess of Courland.

The affair plunged the Duchess into an agony of despair. Envious of her daughter's triumph she began to embarrass Talleyrand with her jealousy. Her angry and violently expressed resentment at being supplanted in his affections by Dorothéa drove him into a frenzy of irritation. Now too, as if so unpleasant a situation was not enough, he was faced by further annoyances from his wife.

Catherine detested Dorothéa de Périgord. Haughtily and with studied pettiness she consistently referred to her as "Madame Edmond." She loathed Talleyrand's niece by marriage as much for her youth as for the passion this new adorer had awakened in her husband's heart. For the tragedy of advancing age and fading beauty terrified Catherine. The realization that she was growing old made her weep like a child for days on end. Indeed, her bad temper really began only when she first discovered that she was growing fat. Poor Catherine. Life had taught her many things, but the gentle art of growing old gracefully was not one of them. So she continued to weep for the bloom of youth and the passing years. Her nerves grew fretful and she was full of complaints. She quarreled with Talleyrand and heaped reproaches on his head for his gross infidelity—censure to which he listened calmly behind a mask of rigid self-control, saying little in reply or defense. But neither his wife's querulous upbraiding nor the Duchess of Courland's despair in the slightest degree quenched the fire of his passion for Dorothéa de Périgord.

Chapter Ten

I

"You are groping about like children when you ought to be walking on stilts. You can do all that you want to; please do all that you can. You know the sign. Have confidence in the one that gives it to you." These words, written by Talleyrand in sympathetic ink, reached the headquarters of the armies of England, Russia, Prussia, and Austria on a small piece of creased and tattered paper. It was that conspirator's final hint to the allies that, with Napoleon's military power smashed by the great Battle of the Nations at Leipzig, the road to Paris lay clear and open before them.

On March 31 Czar Alexander, the King of Prussia, and Prince von Schwarzenberg entered Paris at the head of the allied troops. The war was over. The city had capitulated. The soldiers of the allies marched through strangely silent streets in which only a few white cockades and fluttering handkerchiefs greeted them from the sidewalks. The shadow of Napoleon still hung threateningly over the outskirts of the city. But when they reached the Place Vendôme everything was changed. Here the antinational party, chiefly composed of the nobility, welcomed them with excitement and loud cries of *Vive le roi!* Sosthène de la Rochefoucauld tied a rope around the statue of Napoleon in order to drag it from its column, and in an open carriage a richly gowned lady drove through the streets before the advancing column "singing hymns to the pious Bourbons." It was Catherine de Talleyrand. . . .

The czar took up residence at Talleyrand's house in the Rue Saint-Florentin, and there a conference was held. "Well, here we are at last in the famous Paris," said the Russian emperor.

"Now there are three things we can do: we can treat with the Emperor Napoleon, we can establish a regency, or recall the Bourbons."

"The czar is wrong," replied Talleyrand. "There are not three things we can do: there is only one, and that is the last he has mentioned."

Two days later Napoleon was formally deposed by the Senate, a provisional government was set up under Talleyrand, and the French people called to the throne of their country "Louis Stanislas Xavier of France, brother of the last King, and after him other members of the House of Bourbon in the old order." On April 12 Monsieur the Comte d'Artois entered Paris as Lieutenant Governor of the kingdom in the absence of Louis XVIII, whose gout still held him captive in England. The following day Napoleon was compelled to accept the Treaty of Fontainebleau and the cold comfort of Elba "in full sovereignty and a pension of two million francs for himself." When at last, three weeks later, Louis himself entered the capital of France, Monsieur de Talleyrand's work in establishing the Restoration was completed. And once again he was Minister of Foreign Affairs.

During these wildly exciting and historic weeks, Talleyrand and Catherine were seldom to be found under the same roof. The last link that had bound them to each other had been severed by Charlotte's marriage to one of Talleyrand's nephews. Now, for the most part, Catherine lived in the mansion in the Rue d'Anjou-Saint-Honoré when she was in Paris, and it was Dorothéa de Périgord who on special occasions, such as the visit of the czar of Russia, acted as hostess in the Rue Saint-Florentin.

Yet, strangely enough, at this period Talleyrand's marriage suddenly caused a new outcrop of sarcasm and malicious taunts. Too many people in the Court of the Restoration remembered him only as the Bishop of Autun. To them his amazing marriage, even after twelve years, still carried the proportions of a juicy scandal. Even the newspapers made ill-disposed jests about it. "Paris, 6th May, 1814. Yesterday after Mass, the Bishop of Autun had the honour of presenting his wife to the son of

Saint Louis," ran a mischievous paragraph in the *Nain jaune,* a jeering pinprick which that paper published as a purported reprint from an English periodical.

Ensconced in a powerful position, Talleyrand could afford to turn a disdainfully deaf ear to the gibes of the new Court, society, and the press. But in the end even his restrained nature revolted against the continuous chastisement, and he proposed himself for the Congress of Vienna. Three plenipotentiaries were appointed to accompany him. It was arranged that his wife would remain in Paris. He was already well on his way to Vienna when Catherine was indiscreetly informed that Dorothéa de Périgord had met him secretly at a country house near Paris and had accompanied him to the Austrian capital.

This disconcerting news, told to her with sugared malice in a crowded drawing room on the afternoon after her husband's departure, made her turn pale. Though she tried to keep calm, she could not disguise her unhappy anxiety. A deep foreboding took possession of her, and when at last she was alone she abandoned herself to tears of jealousy and humiliation. But what could she do? What would be best for her to do? At all costs she must avoid a break with Talleyrand who held the purse strings, and remain quietly and docilely in Paris. Unquestionably that was the wisest course to follow. . . . Years later, in his memoirs, Talleyrand dismissed this incident of his life with a few brief words. "It appeared to me also that it was necessary to make the French Embassy attractive. I then asked my niece, the Comtesse de Périgord, to accompany me and do the honours of my house. By her superior intellect and tact she knew how to please."

So, while Dorothéa was pleasing Talleyrand and the guests at the French embassy at Vienna, Catherine lived through the days in Paris. She speculated on the Exchange and made a considerable income for herself. She was sometimes seen at receptions wearing singularly eccentric clothes, such as "a scarlet cashmire pelisse, secured up the front by a profusion of gold cord and tassels and a gold tissue turban." Society tolerated her with amused indulgence for, when everything had been weighed and considered, one had to remember that this eccentric and rather stout woman who yet carried the remains of her great beauty regally, was still the wife of the most powerful statesman in France.

II

When the discussions of the Congress of Vienna were at their height, the thunder of Napoleon once again resounded across Europe. Escaping from Elba he landed near Cannes and, with less than a thousand men, marched on to Lyons. There he assumed imperial power again. With the army flocking to his standard, he took the road that led to Paris. He met no obstacle on his way. France was entranced with admiration at the miracle of this march. "This is greater than Caesar or Alexander; 'tis Jupiter. This is no longer History; 'tis the most prodigious Fable" —sounded but the echo of men's minds. The Bourbons melted before his advance. A king without an army was no king, and Louis fled on his gouty legs to Ghent, while Talleyrand, maker and destroyer of rulers and governments, hastily left Vienna for Carlsbad, declaring coldly that "the first duty of a diplomat after a congress was to attend to his liver."

On March 20 the Emperor Napoleon, amid scenes of wild and passionate enthusiasm, once again took possession of the Tuileries. The day after his arrival Royalists and generals and even priests flocked to the palace to humble themselves before him. Catherine de Talleyrand, however, was not among the supplicants. At the first clap of thunder that had heralded the Emperor's return, she had disappeared from France.

At this crisis in her life she made the most glaring blunder of her career, for instead of hastening to join her husband either at Vienna or Carlsbad, she fled to London with the idea of remaining there until the destruction of Napoleon had been finally effected by the allies. Actually she had to wait but one hundred days for, with defeat turned into rout at Waterloo,

Napoleon fled to Paris and abdicated for the second time. The wars that had devastated Europe for twenty-two years were at an end; the *Northumberland* carried the little Corsican to St. Helena; Louis XVIII once again sat on the throne of France, and Talleyrand was his Prime Minister.

But now, when Catherine turned longing eyes to her beloved Paris, she found her vision blurred by a dense fog of dissension and unhappiness. Talleyrand would not allow her to return. Concealing his real reason beneath a variety of excuses, he kept her in London while he thought out the best way of ridding himself of her for all time.

Monsieur de Talleyrand was prodigiously tired of his wife. Middle age had made her fat and rather heavy, red in the face, and far from good-tempered. He was still passionately in love with his young, beautiful, witty niece Dorothéa de Périgord, who now did the honors of the Rue Saint-Florentin with, he considered, infinitely more grace and tact than Catherine had ever possessed. In short, there was no longer any room for his wife either in his heart or his house. Her return to Paris would be only an annoyance and embarrassment to him. In the circumstances, therefore, he came to the conclusion that since she was in England, it would be a very good thing if she remained there permanently.

With this decision fixed in his mind he wrote to the Marquis d'Osmond, recently appointed ambassador to London, authorizing him to bring Catherine "to reason" by persuading her to remain in England. Though this commission was not at all to Monsieur d'Osmond's taste, he dared not refuse to execute it, for it was through Talleyrand's influence that he had been assigned the London embassy.

The task proved both difficult and unpleasant. Catherine fumed and fretted. She complained that the Thames fogs did not agree with her health and that it was essential to her well-being that she return to Paris as soon as possible. In the end, however, the pressure brought to bear on her was so great that despite her lamentations she submitted, in part, to her husband's final decision. Her reason was simple enough. Not lacking in common sense she realized that with Dorothéa firmly established in the Rue Saint-Florentin, there could not possibly be room for both herself and "Madame Edmond" under the same roof. On the other hand, any attempt to drive her rival away would not only lead to endless scenes for which she felt unprepared, but would in all probability place her in even a worse light with Talleyrand.

"I am suffering as I deserve for yielding to an impulse of false pride," she told the Marquis d'Osmond's wife one afternoon. "I was aware of the position of Madame Edmond in Talleyrand's house in Vienna, but I did not wish to be a witness to it. This sensitiveness prevented me from joining him, as I should have done when the Emperor's return from Elba obliged me to leave Paris. If I had gone to Vienna instead of London, Monsieur de Talleyrand would have been obliged to receive me. And I know well that he would have received me with great kindness. Whatever he might have felt," she added with acute judgment of her husband's character, "he would have shown no irritation. On the contrary, I know full well that he would have treated me with cordiality. But," she added pathetically, "I had a horror of that woman, to which I yielded, though wrongly. My mistake was that I thought him too weak to dare to send me away. I had not taken into account that a coward may grow courageous in the absence of the enemy! I have made a mistake and must bear the consequences and I do not wish to aggravate the situation by a rebellious attitude. I give in and Monsieur de Talleyrand will find me quite ready to avoid anything that might increase the scandal."

At this moment of her life Catherine de Talleyrand behaved like a great lady indeed. Having once realized that the worst possible injury she could do herself and her husband was to air their private disagreements and miseries in public, she stole the honors of tradition and good breeding from Talleyrand by her calm and judicious conduct. She had made a great blunder, and she resigned herself to bear the results. Talleyrand had closed the gates of Paris in her face. Very well then, for the time being she would not go to Paris. But neither would she stay in London. At all costs she was determined to cross the Channel once again. And she did.

In the spring of 1816 she left England for France and journeyed to Pont-de-Sains, the estate in the Département du Nord, south of Avesnes, which her husband had given her as a marriage settlement. It was her intention to reside at Pont-de-Sains throughout the summer and to spend the winter in Brussels. Talleyrand, fearing the consequences of further protest, allowed her to have her way.

III

But Dorothéa de Périgord was not satisfied. Pont-de-Sains, so close to Avesnes, was very near Paris. What was to prevent Catherine from suddenly reappearing in Talleyrand's household, she demanded. She was quite prepared to keep house for her uncle, but on no account would she tolerate a common parvenu like her aunt. Talleyrand must either rid himself finally and completely of the millstone around his neck or she would leave the Rue Saint-Florentin.

"I have thought a good deal of Madame de Talleyrand's answer," Dorothéa informed him, "which makes me fear that she will walk into your room some fine day. She will say at first that she only means to stay an hour, but wants a personal explanation from you; all in the hope of getting more money. The only proper thing for both of you is that she should remain in England, since Europe is destined to possess this treasure. Looking as she does she can hardly dare to talk of the bad influence of the climate, which she has borne very well several times. It is quite clear that what she wants is to stay in France or the Low Countries. She thinks that in her own interests she ought to be as near Paris as possible! . . . As money is the chief motive of all Madame de Talleyrand's actions, one should always act towards her from that point of view and I will

venture accordingly to give you a piece of advice that will spare
you a public correspondence which would be distasteful to you.
Send someone to her at once. . . . Send Monsieur Perry with a
sort of letter of credit and let him tell Madame de Talleyrand
from you that she shall not touch a farthing of the income
you allow her until she is in England, and that elsewhere she
will not get a halfpenny. Let Monsieur Perry go with her to
Calais or Ostend and stay there until he has seen her embark. I
assure you this is good advice and you will be wrong not to
follow it."

Talleyrand, shuddering at the thought of his wife's reappear-
ance in Paris and terrified at the idea of losing Dorothéa,
screwed his courage to the sticking point and determined to
settle this vexing question once and for all. Though he found
it impossible to follow his niece's advice in toto, he obeyed it
in part by commanding Catherine to remain strictly at Pont-de-
Sains, with the added threat that if she ever dared set foot in
Paris, he would immediately stop her allowance.

This blow to her pride was too much for Catherine. She
rebelled angrily and applied to the Duke of Wellington, begging him to intercede with her husband on her behalf. But
Talleyrand refused to listen to talk of reconciliation. He was
heartily sick of the whole matter. To add to his aggravation,
Paris society, amused by his domestic dissensions, made a popular song out of a stupid quatrain by a topical poetaster in
which his name was joined with that of Chateaubriand:

> *Au diable soient les mœurs! disait Chateaubriand,*
> *Il faut auprès de moi que ma femme revienne.*
> *Je rends grace aux mœurs, répliquait Talleyrand,*
> *Je puis enfin répudier la mienne.*

He refused to be pacified. He felt no sympathy for his wife's
lamentations and insisted that she remain strictly at Pont-de-
Sains or she would feel the consequence of his displeasure.

At this time Catherine wrote pathetically to her friend the

Chevalier Millin: "I can only say that I put all my trust in Providence; gentleness and patience is all that I have ever opposed to the selfishness and harshness with which I am treated." . . . The estrangement from Talleyrand left an aching void in her heart. Lonely and miserable, she begged Millin to pay her a visit at Pont-de-Sains, an invitation which unfortunately he found it impossible to accept at that time.

"I am extremely sorry that you cannot come and breathe the air of the woods, which is said to be very beneficial," she replied to his letter of regret. "It is a real privation for me, monsieur, which I will add to those with which Providence has overwhelmed me since I was obliged to leave my home in March 1815. I shall prolong my stay here as long as the season will permit. I came for the sake of economy, having no horses nor any source of expense, not wishing to contract debts, and having charges to which I consider myself bound, and you know that the pension I receive from the Prince, my husband, is 30,000 francs; and no cherished or valuable article was given to me; and I sold some jewels to buy furniture, china and table napkins, having nothing before me for the tranquillity of my soul but to have patience. Amen. The torrents of bitterness which I have drunk make me indifferent to these petty annoyances."

She was very unhappy and bitterly hurt by her husband's conduct and the crushing blows to her rank and dignity. Yet her letters to friends in Paris were full of questions about Talleyrand. How was he looking? Was he well? Was he in Paris or at Valençay? What *was* going on at her old home in Berry? Her thoughts were often at the Château of Valençay. She dreamed about it at night, longing for it with passionate nostalgia. To Millin she wrote touchingly: "If you should have any pleasant details of the pleasures of Valençay, you know, Monsieur le Chevalier, that Valençay is still as much my home as my present domicile. . . ."

The months passed. She was bored to distraction. There was no joy for her at Pont-de-Sains. The house itself was small—she spoke of it as "this little cottage, for it is really that, and not a château." It stood in the middle of a meadow completely surrounded by a forest. When one looked out of a window one saw nothing but the thick swaying branches of tall trees. There was no other view. The nearest neighbor lived a long way off and stray travelers seldom passed that way. Occasionally the authorities of Avesnes arrived to pay their respects to the Princesse de Bénévent; and once an American woman for whom she had a great affection—the Comtesse Hérachim de Polignac, accompanied by her husband who had secured a place in the Princess' regard "because he is perfect to his wife's family"—came to stay with her for a short while. But visitors were rare, and she dared not even invite her good friend the Duc de San Carlos to cheer her exile. Day followed day and nothing ever seemed to happen at Pont-de-Sains. The most exciting event in months was the stampede of a herd of wild boar through the park one night.

The "little cottage" was a hermit's retreat. Here one could meditate and dream and study in peace. But Catherine was not made for solitude. She could neither meditate nor dream. Hungrily she yearned for the sensual world she loved, the world of society, gaiety, and luxury. She pined and fretted and filled the long weary hours with reading and music, fishing and bathing in "a little river only four feet wide, but the water is very limpid." At last she could bear the ennui of peace and quietude no longer and in a mood of frenzied despair she left Pont-de-Sains in the autumn of 1817.

Her arrival in Paris was quite unexpected. Even Talleyrand had received no warning of her intended return. Perplexed and indignant, he met the ironic mockery of society with haughtiness and satirical contempt. Even the king was made to feel the sting of his tongue. "Is it true that the Princess is back?" Louis asked him one day at a levee, thinking to have a sly little joke of his own at the expense of the grand seigneur's embarrassing position.

Talleyrand met the royal eye arrogantly. How dare that "fat daddy" laugh at him! Had he forgotten how he had run to

Ghent as fast as his gouty legs could carry him on March 19, that day before Napoleon's triumphant reoccupation of the Tuileries? "Nothing is more true, sire," he answered with frigid hauteur, "for it seems that I too had to have my 20th of March!"

Catherine neither forced her way into her old home in the Rue Saint-Florentin nor tried to seek a "personal explanation" from her husband. She adhered to the decision she had made in London not to do anything that would "aggravate the situation." That she was in Paris again meant much to her. In the suburb of Auteuil she rented the villa Beauséjour, and there for a while she sunned herself in Talleyrand's reflected glory. But though they lived so near each other, she never saw her husband again.

If Paris did not assuage the ache in Catherine's heart caused by Talleyrand's treatment of her, it at least cured her of the ennui that had prostrated her at Pont-de-Sains. And she had memories.

BOOK VI

The Last Act

Chapter One

I

The Villa Beauséjour in the suburb of Auteuil which Catherine de Talleyrand, Princesse de Bénévent, rented from Monsieur Beauvais on her return to Paris was a spacious residence surrounded by tall trees and a charming formal garden. To the overwrought princess who had fled from the bleak inhospitality of Pont-de-Sains, this villa seemed a paradise. A very considerable income—in addition to the interest she derived from her personal speculations, Talleyrand made her a liberal allowance—enabled her to live in that style and luxury to which the years had accustomed her. She kept a large staff of servants, employed secretaries and lady companions, entertained lavishly and, on fixed days, received not only members of fashionable society but also savants and men of letters. She labored with painstaking deliberation to make the villa Beauséjour—in the general routine of its household, the hospitality of its table, and the entertainments of its drawing room—an exact replica of Talleyrand's ménage in the days when she was its hostess.

Her appetite was great for the good things of the world, for magnificence and rich living! She could not turn her back upon the world. Peace and seclusion were anathema to her. If she could no longer play the part of Talleyrand's presiding goddess, she determined at least to act the goddess in her own salon. Desperately she clung to the shadow of her former life at the villa Beauséjour. If at times memories of her former glory brought anguish and melancholy, these soon passed.

She tried to forget that she had grown heavy, and instead prided herself on her "air of spirituality." She shut her eyes tightly to the fact that her skin was flushed and very red, and consoled herself that it still remained unwrinkled and looked well by candlelight. She would not and could not realize that Talleyrand and time, the one by withholding the flashlight brilliance of his power and eminence, the other by pilfering her beauty, had stolen her glory and that, without a background and without beauty, she was but a pathetically aging woman who often made herself ridiculous by her arrogance and her absurd preoccupation with her rank.

The years had sadly changed her will-o'-the-wisp whims and fancies into puerile vanities and irrational eccentricities. She often behaved about many things with strange singularity of conduct, but about nothing was she more eccentric than her nobility. She took a childish pride in her title and allowed no one to forget for one moment that she was a princess. In peculiar ways and with overbearing arrogance she demanded that homage be done to her rank. Even the elderly countess of the ancien régime who at one time acted as her companion at the villa Beauséjour was not allowed to forget that she was *only* a countess and that Catherine de Talleyrand was a princess. It was not that Catherine disliked the countess. On the contrary, she was on the friendliest terms with the old lady and extremely fond of her. But she wanted it remembered that there was a time and a place for the expression of this fond friendliness. It happened that whenever she took a walk—and the countess always had to accompany her —there were angry scenes, for she insisted with fiery petulance that in deference to her rank her companion should not walk at her side but must follow at a short distance. If by any chance the old countess approached too close, Madame la Princesse would stop, turn round haughtily and demand, with crushing reproof: *"Comtesse, vous perdez le respect?"*

Yet for all her eccentricities and faults, and she had many, Catherine de Talleyrand was still lovable to those who really understood her. She was a foolish, vain, and arrogant old martinet, but she could, when she liked, be gentle and sympathetic and very tender. She possessed, too, a real and deep appreciation of kindness.

II

Talleyrand at this time was living in retirement, a retirement which was to last for fifteen years. He spent the long winter months in Paris, at his mansion in the Rue Saint-Florentin. His summers, except for occasional visits to Switzerland, the Pyrenees, or his beloved Bourbon-l'Archambault, were passed at Valençay, from which he had effaced all the scars and marks left by the Spanish princes, those unwanted guests of long ago.

At the Rue Saint-Florentin, as at Valençay—where he played the part of country squire, endowed an almshouse and a school and enriched the church with the gift of a belfry—brilliant assemblies still gathered about him. Though he looked like a ghost dragging its leg, he had lost neither his charm of manner nor his sparkle of mind, and as always he could dominate a room full of people by the power of his genius. Old age had made as little difference to the rich, grave tones of his voice as to his habits. He still sought the comfort of his bed only in the small hours of the morning; still rose early; still spent hours over his toilette.

It was at Valençay rather than at the Rue Saint-Florentin that this man who had helped to make history in Europe for forty years held his little court. The château was always full of visitors. Here, as at his Paris mansion, Dorothéa de Périgord with her quick, clever mind and large dark eyes acted as his hostess and never left his side.

The years had made Dorothéa forget the passion she had once felt for a young Austrian count, a passion that had caused her husband's uncle so much unhappiness at the time of the Congress of Vienna. She had sacrificed love for ambition and had gained the distinction of playing Egeria to the most famous and powerful man in France, Charles Maurice de Talleyrand. Edmond de Périgord, her husband, to whom she had borne two sons, had long since ceased to matter in her life. Indeed, she had not lived in his house for many years. In 1820 they were reconciled, but after a short time and to Dorothéa's great gratification Edmond returned to his own life and she to hers with Talleyrand. At Valençay she became "spiritual with pregnancy," and there she gave birth to a daughter whom she called Pauline. So passionately devoted to the child was Talleyrand that eager-tongued gossip, with jest and snigger, crowned him at the age of nearly seventy with the honor of progeniture. . . .

But time was speeding on. Each passing year took toll of friends and enemies who had formed the web and woof of Talleyrand's existence. In 1817 Madame de Staël died. Four years later Madame de Rémusat, whose happy friendship he had won in the days of the Consulate, and the Duchess of Courland whom once he had loved so passionately and who had lived to see her place in his affections taken by her daughter Dorothéa, were laid in their graves. In this same year, too, on the rocky island of St. Helena, remote from the scene of his triumphs, the Little Corsican died.

Talleyrand was one of the guests in a crowded drawing room on the night the report of Napoleon's death reached Paris. For a moment after the announcement had been made it seemed as if no one breathed. Men and women stiffened in their chairs and sat strangely dumb. The silence was shattered by the uttering of three words. "What an event!" someone exclaimed.

"It is no longer an event, it is only a piece of news," a rich, grave voice said quietly in a far corner of the room. Talleyrand had spoken. . . .

In the year 1828, the Duc de San Carlos, who had played so strange a part in Catherine's life, died. When Talleyrand was told the news he seemed deeply touched, so much so that his informant interrupted his expressions of regret by remarking with dry malice: "He was certainly a fine man, Monsieur de Talleyrand, but I did not know you were so attached to him."

"I will explain," said Talleyrand. "The Duc de San Carlos was my wife's lover; he was an honorable man and gave her good advice. I don't know into whose hands she will fall now."

How fiercely that affair of long ago still rankled in his mind!

Had he ever really believed that the gallant Spaniard was his wife's lover? Talleyrand always wore a mask and believed anything that suited his purpose. He could be bitter, cruel, and merciless in his cynicism. Heartlessly he uttered those words: "I don't know into whose hands she will fall now," for he knew very well that Catherine at this time and in this, her sixty-sixth year, was living in sad loneliness, and that her thoughts ever turned only inward and backward, to the past and to him.

With shuffling feet the cavalcade of death passed on its way, yet still a noble band of devoted satellites remained to light the earthly road along which old Talleyrand limped. Montrond still chattered wittily although a little wheezily; the Countess Tyskiewitz's glass eye shone with its old adoration; Dorothéa was still his splendid Egeria and Pauline his "guardian angel" . . . There was so much to remind him of the past. . . . As if his mind was not already a rich storeroom of remembrances, he opened the doors of his house wide to young Delacroix, the painter, son of that Madame Delacroix who had been ousted from his affections so many years ago by Madame Grand, the courtesan. And he named his favorite spaniel "Carlos" in memory of a once dashing Spanish don.

III

Catherine, too, had her memories, but for the most part they were sad because she sat bowed in melancholy despair. Separation from Talleyrand had broken her spirit. His withdrawal from her life had left a vacuum which, try as she might, nothing seemed to fill. Slowly but surely as the years slipped by she sank into an old age of physical suffering and loneliness. Year by year, too, death took those whom once she had known and loved, and who had helped to form the curious pattern of her life.

In England, in 1818, just four months after the passing of his old enemy Warren Hastings, Sir Philip Francis died "almost in his sleep," at the age of seventy-eight. Catherine had not seen him for close on sixteen years, not since before her marriage with

Talleyrand. During her last migration to England, at the time of the Hundred Days, he had made no effort to visit her—"the dread of losing his recollections of her in sad realities prevented him from wishing to see or be seen by her . . . as he heard from those of his friends who had renewed their acquaintance . . . that it was impossible to recognize all those Venus-like charms which were celebrated from the Indus to the Ganges and inspired his muse on the Banks of the Seine and the Thames." . . . Now he was dead, Philip Francis who, by his desire for her, had set her feet upon the road she was to follow for so many years. Catherine wept for him and for an old passion so long kept fragrant by the potpourri of memory.

Two years later George François Grand, who had made a child wife of the little daughter of Pierre Werlée, was buried at the Cape of Good Hope. He had married again, and was happy in his second marriage, though never with life as a whole. The Consulting Councillorship to the Batavian Republic, which Catherine had obtained for him in the year of her marriage to Talleyrand, had terminated when the Cape was taken over by the British in 1806.

Then the new English Governor had appointed him to the post of Inspector of H.M.'s Woods and Lands. This office he had retained for only a short time. No further appointment followed the loss of this post, and poor, grumbling, quarrelsome Grand spent the remainder of his life at the Cape inundating successive governors with boisterous letters demanding favored employment and innumerable indulgences. Much of his time, too, he gave to writing his *Narrative,* published in 1814, in which he told the whole story of his life so "chequered with vicissitudes."

When his last will and testament was opened after his death a codicil was found attached to it. "Finally I request my first wife, since the Princess of Talleyrand," ran a paragraph of this supplementary note, "to extend a Portion of the annuity which, out of Consideration and Regard for my conduct towards her during my prosperous career in life, she tendered in my adversity, viz: as is comprised in my *Narrative,* a handsome pension for life

to enjoy where I pleased. I entreat her with my last Breath to allow half the said amount to my present and second wife, during
her life and in the assurance of the sentiments and goodness which
during a happy time I experienced with my first wife that she
was blessed with, I comfort myself whilst still living, that my
Prayer and Entreaty to Her will not have been made in vain."

IV

At this time Catherine had moved from the villa Beauséjour
at Auteuil and had taken a house in Paris itself, in the Rue de
Lille. Here for several years she entertained on the same scale as
she had done at the villa. Flatterers still gathered about her. In
their servile words she found a certain comfort, for they reminded her of the days of her glory and made her forget the
weight and pain of her aging body. Still, as ever, she was pathetically blinded by the proud dignity of her rank, and still she
played the haughty, arrogant princess.

Every year, on the king's birthday in August she gave a party.
Poets, savants, and people of society sat at her table; foreigners,
especially Englishmen, were invited to her house; and in her
drawing room many an author, anxious to secure an audience,
gave the first reading of his unpublished work. In 1822, Viennet
declaimed his new tragedy *Achille* at one of her receptions and,
during his two years of exile, Thomas Moore, the poet who had
fled from England to evade arrest, was a frequent visitor at the
Rue de Lille. Many a night he delighted his hostess and her assembled guests with recitals of his poetry. For Catherine was still
striving desperately to imitate the splendor she had once known
in Talleyrand's salon.

The routine of her household was modeled with scrupulous
exactness on that of the Rue Saint-Florentin, and almost everything about her spoke of her memories of the days of her grandeur. The past had become her mania. Deliberately she packed
every room of her house with eloquent witnesses to her undying

remembrance of her former magnificence. Wherever she looked, symbols of bygone days met her eyes. The clock on the mantelpiece, her favorite armchair, the rug before the fireplace, the embroidered cushion on which she rested her feet, even the lawn handkerchief she held in her hand—all were conspicuously decorated with the emblem and the *Re que Diou* of the Talleyrand armorial device. The little cage in which she kept her much-loved pets, a pair of snow-white dormice, was an exact model of the Château of Valençay, exquisitely made and perfect in every detail of dome and towers.

In her memory Valençay shone as the most priceless jewel in the diadem of her departed greatness. She carried its picture in her heart. The château had become the altar of her lost happiness. She never spoke of it without weeping, yet desired to speak of it often. She would sit for hours recounting the joys she had once experienced there, even the least of them, and delving into her memory, she would explain the genealogy of every family on the neighboring estates with the greatest care and deliberation. Vividly she recalled every detail of her life at Valençay and of the château itself—the parklands and the rivers, the deep moat and the high towers, the lilac-scented alleys and the cooing wood pigeons, the names of the curé and the maire and of the meanest provincial she had known.

Her love for Valençay was almost fanatical in its fervor. She had been so happy there as the wife of France's greatest diplomat —the mighty Talleyrand, whom she had last seen on the day when he set out in a carriage for the Congress of Vienna. Years had passed since that day, and these had dulled her anguish and resentment of his treatment. There was no longer bitterness in her heart against him. Indeed, she had begun to yearn for him and to think tenderly of this man who had ceased to love her so long ago.

She now took the most touching interest in everything connected with him and with his life. She never tired of asking questions, or of listening to the smallest crumb of news about the Rue Saint-Florentin and Valençay. She spoke of him eagerly and always with sincere and unaffected admiration, praising his great talents and brilliance, and never by so much as a word condemning his treatment of her. Through the fading years and the mists of memory she seemed to see her husband anew, with a halo of her own making about his head.

To Talleyrand, however, in spite of the years, his wife remained a disturbing element. She was out of his life and yet in it. He longed to lay the ghost and could not. The allowance he made her, with secret unwillingness but punctilious regularity, served to keep her fresh in his memory. Still, he was prepared to forgive her her existence provided she behaved like a well-trained and obedient ghost and flitted only through the thin air on the far horizon of his life.

Since certain circumstances prevented him from erasing her completely from his mind he was quite courteous and attentive to her—at a distance. Regularly on certain annual festivals, such as New Year's Day or when he heard she was suffering from some slight indisposition, he sent members of his household to call and pay their respects to her, and always they came heavily laden with polite and elegantly worded messages of good wishes from the Prince. Catherine, Princesse de Talleyrand, who had once demanded so much of him, now accepted these crumbs of his favor with pathetic joy. She had grown so lonely. Year by year, as the company in her drawing room dwindled, she became a little sadder, a little more dejected. She was often ill. She realized only too well that she was being neglected and forsaken by the gay society she had once so deeply loved. To the few close friends who remained loyal to her she clung tenaciously, and these and her still burning pride and vanity in her nobility cheered her darkening days.

Chapter Two

I

Slowly the magnificent coffin was lowered into the vault. Four dukes in glittering uniforms covered it with the flags of four companies of Guards. The hand of justice, the scepter and the crown were placed upon the draped ensigns and upon these a sword, gauntlets, spurs, a breastplate, and a shield, which had never been worn in battle, were next thrown down. Then came a solemn, momentary pause and a shriveled old man limped clumsily toward the open vault, stooped, and with great dignity covered the coffin with the national standard. Talleyrand, the aged Prince de Bénévent, had paid his last act of fealty to the Bourbon Louis XVIII, whom he had helped restore to the throne of France. The following year this almost fabulous old man, who had been present at the coronation of Louis XVI in 1774, journeyed again to the city of Rheims to play an important part in the crowning of Charles X.

Talleyrand at this time was still living in virtual retirement, yet five years later, when the reactionary reign of Charles X drew to its hazardous end, it was he who once again formed the center of the secret plottings that fomented a new revolution and brought a new king to the throne of France.

On July 28, 1830, the tricolor once more starred the streets of Paris, through which the inflamed mob surged on its way to the Hôtel de Ville. On the 29th, with the storming of the Louvre and the Tuileries and the insurrection of the troops, the people again made themselves masters of Paris. Now Monsieur Thiers, the journalist, set the city ablaze with his public proclamations demanding the abdication of Charles X in favor of Égalité's son. . . .

Ten days later Louis Philippe, the Citizen Monarch, was proclaimed king of France. And Talleyrand crossed the Channel as Ambassador to London. Dorothéa, now the Duchesse de Dino, accompanied her uncle on his mission to England. He never moved a step without his loyal and inspiring Dorothéa. His company still gave such endless delight, and she was so charming, that soon they made a unique niche for themselves in English society. At this time William IV sat on the throne of England; that clever gentleman Lord Palmerston was Foreign Secretary; and young Benjamin Disraeli was working his way to Parliament through the drawing rooms of London.

With but a few short breaks, Talleyrand remained in England for four years. Then at last, having formed the Quadruple Alliance in firm communion with Palmerston, he returned to Paris. It was 1834. He had served his country for more than half a century. He resigned from office and left public life forever. His health was failing. He was a crippled old man of eighty who had outlived his generation. Most of the companions and loves of his youth were dead. Even the ever-devoted Countess Tyskiewitz, one of the last human monuments of his past, had recently died at Tours. In sorrow he interred her at his beloved Valençay, where he had enjoyed so many years of her almost fanatically loyal friendship.

Yet, despite age and failing health, he had many compensations. His sight was perfect, his hearing unimpaired. He could still fascinate a whole assembly with the charm of his manner and the brilliance of his mind. Still wheezy, witty old Montrond was his friend, and still Dorothéa was his muse, and Pauline his "guardian angel."

II

But Catherine, living in loneliness in her house in the Rue de Lille, renamed the Rue de Bourbon since the Restoration, had nothing to compensate her for the dying years. She had become a sick and broken old woman, so ponderously fat that she could scarcely walk. In her large blue eyes lay a dull, apathetic look. She suffered grievously from indigestion and was almost always ill. She suffered, too, because, realizing that she was being forgotten by the world, she felt herself piteously deserted and abandoned.

She still had a circle of friends, but it had dwindled sadly. Often she sat down at her table with only her lady companions—a table richly laid with fine dishes and good foods which she dared not eat. She slept a great part of the day. Now sleep was to her the best thing in life—and when she slept she snored heavily, noisily. The dying years lay about her. She lived only in memories of the days when she was queen of Talleyrand's salon. Occasionally she still received visitors, but only very occasionally, and then, roused temporarily from the deep gloom of depression into which she had sunk, she spoke only of the past.

Alone with her thoughts and the shadows of glory, she sat in her richly furnished house, a taciturn, half-forgotten old woman with large, wistful eyes. Sometimes she thought of death. . . . George Grand, Philip Francis, Edouard Dillon, San Carlos, Lambertye, Spinola, and Delessart—they were all dead. Napoleon and Fouché, the Red Partridge, the Duchess of Courland, Madame de Staël and the old Countess Tyskiewitz—dead, dead, dead. Where was generous Thomas Lewin, and what had happened to gallant Nathaniel Belchier? . . . But Talleyrand still lived, Talleyrand and the "Countess Edmond" whom people now called the Duchess de Dino. How she hated that woman!

Catherine seldom spoke, and when she did it was always of Talleyrand and the years of her glory or of what was passing in his house. She was deeply concerned about everything connected with him. Her interest was so concentrated, so intense, that it was actually an obsession. She insisted that the routine of her house, to its smallest detail, should be strictly regulated in accordance with that practiced at the Rue Saint-Florentin. Even her diet, and the times at which she took her meals, were subjected to this same stern law of imitation. With so much vehemence and accuracy did she persist in this mania that at one time she became seriously ill as a result of her scrupulous observance of Talley-rand's habits—in particular his practice of eating only one meal a day, although this did not prevent her from gaining weight.

Yet, though she was old and forlorn and often ill, Catherine would rouse herself ponderously to play the dignified hostess and great princess when rare visitors called or Talleyrand sent a member of his household to inquire after her health. Then, very graciously, she would receive in her drawing room, regally seated in a high-backed chair that bore the arms and motto of the Talleyrand family, her back to a window, her head and neck beautifully poised, the folds of her magnificent gown neatly arranged about her feet which rested on a monogrammed stool.

A sort of muslin coiffure covered most of her hair—that once luxuriant head of golden hair. It had turned quite gray except for one solitary golden strand, last emblem of her lyrical beauty. Chin straps of white ribbon were attached to her headdress and these concealed her cheeks and neck and made her face look infinitely small. The effect was by no means unbecoming, for not only did these bands of ribbon and muslin hide the wrinkled ravages of time, but somehow, strangely, they seemed to give even greater grandeur of mien to this extremely dignified old lady.

The drawing room in which the Princess received her guests was always shrouded in soft, tempered light. If the day was very bright, the shutters on the window behind her chair were partly closed, leaving only a narrow slit through which a ray of sunlight might slip to play with the one remaining golden streak upon her head. For Catherine de Talleyrand was still vain, still hungry for praise and delicate flattery, still blindly proud of her nobility.

Chapter Three

I

The summer of 1835 was drawing to its close. A year had gone by since Talleyrand's renouncement of public life and service. The aged prince was far from well. The passing of so many of his contemporaries—particularly the Countess Tyskiewitz—had affected him deeply and left a poignant impression on his mind. Much of his old gaiety and spirit had vanished. He was often languid and depressed and spoke with melancholy despondency of death and the cessation of his life.

His ill-health made him nervous and gloomy. He was unduly anxious about himself and extremely agitated by the fact that there was a perceptible pause at every sixth beat of his pulse. Frequently Dorothéa de Dino would find him alone in his study, engrossed in reading medical books on heart disease. She was gravely concerned about his mental and physical debility, when one morning in October a message was brought to the Rue Saint-Florentin that the Princesse de Talleyrand was lying at death's door as the result of a stroke. Dorothéa's anxiety turned to acute alarm. Would there be another death and must she again break the news to Talleyrand? How would he react to it in his present condition? What consequences would follow? She was not so much afraid of the actual shock of bereavement, for she knew quite well that "his heart is not interested," but she was terrified that the passing of "a person much of his own age, with whom he had lived and of whom he had once been fond, or who had been so indispensable to him that he had given her his name," would aggravate his ill health.

For a long time she sat in her room debating whether to tell him the tidings she had received early that morning. At last she decided that it would, perhaps, be best to prepare him for what was coming. So she went to him. Tactfully she spoke of a number of things, and from these worked around to that which lay uppermost in her mind. In an indirect way she gave him to understand that his wife was dying. He listened quietly while she talked, without interruption, without showing the slightest emotion of any kind. When she ceased to speak he broke the silence that followed not by comment on what he had just heard but by changing the subject and talking of something else.

All that day he never mentioned Catherine's danger. But the next day he spoke of it almost incessantly—not sorrowfully, but calmly and dispassionately, and not of Catherine herself but only of the various arrangements that would have to be made if she died, of the funeral, of the cards to be sent out. Repeatedly he complained that it would be "an embarrassment to be in mourning." Never once, by a single word or the slightest tremor of a nerve, did he express grief or regret. He did not feign what he did not feel. Nothing was left of his love. He was conscious only of relief. If Catherine died he would be released from a duty. With her passing the one scandal in his life that he had never been able to live down would at last disappear. "If the Princess dies," he told Dorothéa calmly, again and again, "I shall go out of Paris for a week or a fortnight."

For hours he busied himself with certain financial questions that would arise at Catherine's death, for with her passing he would regain possession not only of the comfortable allowance he had made to her annually but also of certain moneys in which she had a life interest. He took no pains to hide either the gratification he felt at the possibility of once again owning this wealth, or the pleasure and satisfaction he took in the thought that in the eyes of the Church, if Catherine died, he would no longer be a married priest. All day he was calm and serene. He had not been in such a tranquil mood for a long time. At moments, even, he seemed quite gay, and once Dorothéa de Dino caught him humming a little tune.

"Is it the fact that you will soon be a widower that puts you in such good spirits?" she asked him.

He looked at her quizzically and pulled a funny face like an impudent, mischievous child. Then glibly he went on talking—of all the things that would have to be done if Catherine died and how pleasant it would be to have an increased income. . . . But Catherine did not die. She recovered sufficiently to be able to sit in her high-backed chair again and to receive the messengers he sent to her house with courteous inquiries after her health.

Relentlessly the clock on her mantelpiece with its coat of arms and its *Re que Diou* ticked away the minutes of the dying year. The trees in the Champs-Élysées turned yellow with autumn sickness. A cold wind scattered the seared submissive leaves. Rain fell and December came.

II

The parlor of the nuns of Saint-Michel in the Rue Saint-Jacques where Monseigneur de Quélen, Archbishop of Paris, was giving an ecclesiastical audience, was warm and bright with the light of many burning candles. Outside it was bleak and cold and dark on this December evening at six o'clock. A sudden stir and whispering at the parlor door disturbed the Archbishop's speech. Someone came hurriedly forward to inform him that a lady who had just arrived wished to see him urgently, most urgently. She had a message for him from a dying person. Would he speak to her? . . . Since it was so urgent, he would see her instantly. He asked that she be brought to him. A moment later the Duchess d'Esclignac, daughter of Baron Boson de Talleyrand-Périgord, second brother of the fabulous old Prince de Talleyrand, entered the room.

"Monseigneur, forgive me," she apologized breathlessly. "But my aunt . . . She is dying."

"Your aunt, Duchess?"

"The Princesse de Talleyrand, Monseigneur."

The Archbishop inclined his head.

"She is asking for you," the Duchess continued hurriedly. "She

wishes to make her confession, but desires to make her acknowl-
edgment of sin to no one but you, Monseigneur. I pray you,
forgive me for this intrusion. I had to speak with you, for there
is not a moment to lose. The doctors say she will not last the
night. . . ."

Monseigneur de Quélen dismissed the audience. A few minutes
later, with his two Grand Vicars, the Abbé Affre and the Abbé
Quentin, he was on his way in the Duchess' carriage to save that
passing soul in the Rue de Bourbon which once had been called
the Rue de Lille. Beside him the Duchess sat dabbing her eyes
with a small damp handkerchief. She was deeply distressed, for
between herself and her aunt, the Princesse de Talleyrand, there
was a real bond of affection and understanding.

III

The room where Catherine lay dozing on her bed near the window was shrouded in subdued light. Only the candles in two tall
silver candelabra—one at the head of her bed shedding a pool of
light on her drawn, strangely blue-gray face—dispelled the darkness. She was quite alone; she had asked to be alone so that she
might put her thoughts in order before making her confession.

At Monseigneur de Quélen's entrance she raised herself ponderously from her pillows and in a low whisper thanked him for
coming to her so readily. She was deeply moved at seeing him and
the effort of raising herself exhausted her. She sank back heavily,
her eyes closed, her breathing labored. It took some moments be-
for she was able to speak. "Monseigneur, what I am about to
say—I should like to repeat before my friends. Will you be so
kind, my lord, and call them in—all of them—the Duchess
d'Esclignac, the Comtesse de Champeron, the Marquise de Vins
de Pezac, and my two lady's maids. They are in the next room. I
desired that they should leave me alone for a while, so that I
might prepare myself for this moment."

They came, her friends and her servants, and gathered about

her bed, and with them came the two Grand Vicars. Propped up against her pillows Catherine sat looking at them, looking at one face, then another. For a long time she did not speak. She remained silent, her heart too full for words, seeing the tears in the eyes that her eyes sought. Her lips trembled. "My friends," she whispered. "My friends." The words echoed like a sigh through the room.

But suddenly she spoke in a firmer, an almost resolute voice. "Monseigneur, they are all here," she said. "And this is what I wish to say before them. That I am glad to be reconciled to God, and after asking His pardon, I beg pardon of men for any scandal I have caused." A sigh escaped hissingly from her parted lips. Her eyelids flickered and closed. She lay very still, exhausted by the effort she had made.

Monseigneur turned to the Abbé Quentin and bade him go to the Church of St. Thomas d'Aquin to fetch the Eucharist and the holy oils. The Abbé departed hurriedly. No sooner had he left the room than Catherine roused herself from her half stupor and begged to speak in private to Monseigneur de Quélen.

"Am I indeed dying, my lord, and is there no hope for me?" she asked him when the others had withdrawn and they were quite alone.

He answered her "out of the fullness of his benevolent heart," tried to comfort her with vague hope, and urged her to put her trust in God and hold fast to her faith and love for Him. Monseigneur was most kind, but in his words of gentle encouragement she read the truth and knew that her end was near. She remained quite calm, showed no sign of distress. Quietly she asked him to send for two caskets that she kept locked in an iron chest. When these were brought to her—one of red morocco, the other of wood, both neatly tied with white silk ribbon and sealed in wax with her arms, the armorial design of the Talleyrand-Périgords—she gave them to him with her own hands.

"Monseigneur, I give these to you for safekeeping," she said. "If I get well"—for a second a smile flitted across her lips—

"if I get well, you will give them back to me. If not, I beg that you will give them to my dear niece, the Duchesse d'Esclignac." She drew a sheaf of francs in banknotes from under her pillow. "And these—these are for the poor. Two thousand francs."

"May I say that you wish to devote them to the relief of cholera orphans?" he asked.

"Gladly, Monseigneur. Gladly." For a moment she lay quietly watching him as he placed the caskets and the money on a small table. When he turned to her again she said: "I have one more favor to beg of you, my lord. Will you yourself recommend all who are in my service to the kindness of the Prince de Talleyrand? You, yourself?"

"I will, my daughter."

"To the kindness of the Prince de Talleyrand. The Prince de Talleyrand," she repeated, lingering over the name of the man who was her husband and whom she had not seen for more than twenty years. Then rousing herself as if from a dream, she said in a firm voice: "I am ready to receive the Sacraments of the Church, my lord."

Monseigneur de Quélen left her to assemble her thoughts and went from the room to see whether Abbé Quentin and the curé of St. Thomas d'Aquin had arrived with the Viaticum and the holy oils. They were waiting for him in the adjoining chamber. Some little while later, he came to Catherine again and she made her confession. He showed her the Host, counseled her to trust in God, exhorted her to patience, submissiveness, reverence, and faith, administered the Eucharist and Extreme Unction, and repeated the prayers for the dying. He was still reciting the prayers when, utterly exhausted, she fell asleep. They let her sleep and awakened her later to tell her that her notary, for whom she had sent, was waiting in the drawing room to certify certain deeds and documents. As it was now nine o'clock at night the Archbishop and his two Grand Vicars withdrew and left the dying woman with her friends.

Catherine lived two days longer. She knew there was no hope for her and patiently, without complaint, she waited for the end. She was fully conscious and strangely serene. In the small hours of the morning of December 10 a fit of choking suddenly seized her. The nurse who sat watching at her side tried to make her sip a few drops of water. But she could no longer swallow. The awful sweat of agony broke out on her face, framed in its disheveled profusion of white hair. The room grew dark about her. She could no longer see the flickering candles. Her head fell forward on her chest. Her lips moved. "I am dying," she whispered.

It was a quarter to four in the morning. Catherine de Talleyrand sighed and passed away.

IV

Talleyrand himself was ill at this time and confined to his house in the Rue Saint-Florentin. When the news of Catherine's death was brought to Dorothéa de Dino early in the morning, she shrank from breaking it to him for, though he had shown so little emotion on the previous occasion when his wife lay in grave danger, she greatly feared that this moment of death in its reality would shock him deeply.

She was relieved that he was still asleep when the messenger came, resting quietly after a slight heart attack which had "abated on the application of mustard to his legs." This gave her time to put her thoughts in order, to plan how best to break the news to him. But Dorothéa de Dino distressed herself quite unnecessarily at the anticipation of her painful duty, for when Talleyrand woke from his sleep and she told him, tactfully and very gently, that his princess was dead, he showed no agitation, no remorse. "That simplifies my position very much," was the only comment that he made.

All that day he wore a little smile. He felt tranquil and at peace with the world. A fat old woman had died and he would be the richer for her death. Only of this did he think. Not one thought did he give to the woman whose beauty, almost half a century ago, had thrown him, limping, at her feet. . . . But if Talleyrand would not allow his mind to dwell on her, her passing did touch the heart of another who had once loved her—and gallantly. In distant England old Thomas Lewin, now eighty-two years old, wrote in his diary on December 15, 1835: "Heard that the Princesse Talleyrand was dead." For a long time, it is said, he sat staring at those words. Perhaps he was dreaming of his youth and of the woman who had inspired one of its sweetest interludes.

V

For Catherine de Talleyrand, Princesse de Bénévent, whom the Church still called the widow of George François Grand, a solemn service was held on December 12, 1835, in the Church of St. Thomas d'Aquin. Talleyrand, who had not once been present at her bedside during the days of her illness, did not appear at the funeral rites and ceremonies. His confidential agent Monsieur Demion, who had arranged all matters connected with the obsequies, represented the aged prince at the funeral and watched the body of "Catherine, widow of George François Grand, *connue civilement comme Princesse de Talleyrand*," aged seventy-four, laid to rest in the cemetery of Montparnasse.

Bibliography

Album Perdu (Extracts). Anecdotes relating to Talleyrand, attributed to H. de Thabaud de Latouche. Paris, 1829.

Aus dem Eheleben eines Bischofs. Leipzig, 1884.

BARRAS, COMTE DE. *Memoirs.* 4 vols. London: Osgood McIlvaine & Co., 1895.

BESANT, SIR WALTER. *London in the 18th Century.* London: Chatto & Windus, 1893.

BLECHYNDEN, K. *Calcutta: Past & Present.* London, 1905.

BLENNERHASSET, LADY. *Talleyrand.* 2 vols. London: John Murray, 1894.

BOIGNE, COUNTESS DE. *Memoirs.* 3 vols. London: William Heinemann, 1907.

BRIFAUT, CHARLES. *Souvenirs d'un Académicien.* 2 vols. Paris, 1921.

BULWER, HENRY LYTTON. *Historical Characters: Talleyrand, etc.* 2 vols. London: Richard Bentley, 1868.

BUSTEED, H. E. *Echoes from Old Calcutta.* London: W. Thacker & Co., 1897.

CAREY, W. H. *Good Old Days of the Hon'ble John Company.* 2 vols. Calcutta: R. Cambray & Co., 1906.

CHASTENAY, MADAME DE. *Mémoires* (1771–1815). 2 vols. Paris: Alphonse Roserot, 1896.

COLMACHE, E. *Reminiscences of Prince Talleyrand.* 2 vols. London: Henry Colburn, 1848.

COOPER, RT. HON. ALFRED DUFF. *Talleyrand.* London: Jonathan Cape, 1932.

COTTON, SIR EVAN (H.E.A.). "Madame Grand." (Reprint from *Bengal: Past & Present,* vol. XLVI, 1933.)

COTTON, SIR EVAN (H.E.A.). *Calcutta Old & New.* Calcutta: W. Newman & Co., 1907.

COTTON, J. J. "Madame Grand." *Macmillan's Magazine,* September, 1900.

DINO, DUCHESS DE. *Memoirs.* London: William Heinemann, 1909–10.

FAY, ELIZA. *Original Letters from India* (1779–1815). London: Hogarth Press, 1925.

Female Revolutionary Plutarch, The. London, 1806.

FRANCIS, SIR PHILIP. *Memoirs.* 2 vols. London, 1867.

FRÉNILLY, BARON DE. *Recollections* (1768–1828). London, William Heinemann, 1909.

"GOLDBORNE, SOPHIA." *Hartly House, Calcutta* (A novel). Calcutta: Thacker, Spink & Co., 1908.

GONCOURT, E. and J. DE. *The Woman of the 18th Century.* London: G. Allen & Unwin, 1928.

GRAND, GEORGE FRANÇOIS. *The Narrative of a Gentleman Long Resident in India.* The first English book printed at the Cape of Good Hope, 1814.

GRAND, GEORGE FRANÇOIS. *Last Will and Testament.* In the Archives, Cape Town, Republic of South Africa.

GRANDMAISON, GEOFFREY DE. *L'Espagne et Napoleon.* Paris, 1908.

———. "Les Princes d'Espagne à Valencay," *Le Correspondant,* May 25, 1900.

GRANDPRÈ. *Voyage in the Indian Ocean and to Bengal in the Year 1780.*

GUYOT, RAYMOND. *Le Directoire et la Paix de l'Europe.* Paris, 1903.

———. "Madame Grand à Paris." *Feuilles d'Histoire,* vol. 1, 1909.

HALLAY, ANDRÉ. An article on Madame de Talleyrand in the *Journal des Débats,* February 22, 1901.

HEBER. *Narrative of a Journey Through the Upper Provinces of India.* 2 vols. London: John Murray, 1828.

HICKEY, WILLIAM. *Memoirs.* 4 vols. London: Hurst & Blackett, 1913.

IMPEY, SIR ELIJAH. *Memoirs.* London, 1846.

KIELMANNSEGGE, GRÄFIN. *Memoiren.* Dresden, 1927.

LACOMBE, B. DE. *Talleyrand the Man.* London: Herbert & Daniel, 1910.

LACOUR-GAYET, GEORGES. *Talleyrand* (1754–1838). London, 1904.

LEBRUN, MADAME VIGÉE. *Memoirs.* London: Grant & Richards, 1904.

LEVESON-GOWER, LORD GRANVILLE. *Extracts from Private Correspondence* (1781–1821). 2 vols. London: John Murray, 1916.

PASQUIER, CHANCELIER. *Mémoires.* Paris, 1830.

POTOCKA, LA COMTESSE. *Mémoires.* Paris, 1897.

REMACLE, LE COMTE LOUIS. *Relations Secretes des Agents de Louis XVIII* (1802–1803). Paris, 1899.

RÉMUSAT, MADAME DE. *Memoirs.* London: S. Low & Co., 1895.

SEELEY, L. B. (ed.). *Fanny Burney and Her Friends.* London: Seeley & Co., 1895.

STANHOPE, PHILIP DORMER. *The Genuine Memoirs of Asiaticus.* London, 1784.

TALLEYRAND, CHARLES MAURICE DE. *Memoirs.* 5 vols. London: Griffith & Farran, 1891.

VARS, BARON DE. *Les Femmes de M. de Talleyrand.* Paris, 1891.

VILLEMAREST, C. M. DE. *Life of Prince Talleyrand.* 4 vols. London, 1834–36.

Also

Michaud's *Biographie Universelle.*

Revue Historique de la France.

Indian Historical Records Commission, vol. V.

The Chandernagore Papers (1778–1783).

The Calcutta Review, 1844.

Hicky's *Bengal Gazette* (1780–1782).

Index

273

Annette Joelson

was born in the village of Hopetown, situated near the Orange River in what was then called the Cape Colony. On a farm not far from this village the first diamond was picked up in South Africa.

She spent the first twelve years of her life on a farm in this district of the Great Karoo and was educated at home. She was then sent as a boarding student to the Good Hope Seminary, one of the oldest girls' schools in Cape Town, some 600 miles from her home. Later she entered the University of Cape Town where she took an arts degree.

She always wanted to be a writer and wrote continually during her youth. In 1926, after winning first prize in a South African short story competition, she began to submit articles and stories for publication. During the succeeding ten years many of these appeared in South Africa and in England. During this period, too, her books for children and her five novels were published.

Later she was editor of a woman's magazine in Cape Town and during this time she visited England on two occasions and traveled on the continent. Returning from one of these trips, she taught for a year at the Observatory Girls' High School at the Cape. Just before the outbreak of World War II she broadcast a number of talks for the South African Broadcasting Company, including a series on South African history.

In 1942 Miss Joelson married Maurice Jacobs, a naval officer she had met on a visit to England eight years before and who, then in command of a minesweeper, was passing through Cape Town on his way to the Middle East. A year later she was able to join her husband at his base in East Africa. During this year she worked on the memoirs of G. W. H. Kohler, father of the modern wine industry in South Africa, was a feature writer for an East African newspaper, and again taught school, this time in the Usumbara Mountain district of Tanganyika.

In 1944 when her husband again passed through Cape Town, she joined him on a transport for England. After the war, with her husband back at his post as a merchant banker, she did a series of talks that were broadcast to South Africa over the B.B.C.

In addition to writing, attending the theater, exploring London and the English countryside on foot with her husband, Annette Joelson manages to travel some part of each year. Her recent journeys have taken her to the Baltic, to Greece on several occasions, and to the United States.

DATE DUE

GAYLORD